Pre-twentieth Century Literature

Selected and edited by

Paul Roberts

Oxford University Press

Oxford University Press, Great Clarendon Street, Oxford OX2 6DP

Oxford New York
Athens Auckland Bangkok Bogota Bombay Buenos Aires
Calcutta Cape Town Dar es Salaam Delhi
Florence Hong Kong Istanbul Karachi
Kuala Lumpur Madras Madrid Melbourne
Mexico City Nairobi Paris Singapore
Taipei Tokyo Toronto

and associated companies in
Berlin Ibadan

Oxford is a trade mark of Oxford University Press

© Selection and activities: Paul Roberts

ISBN 0 19 831200 8

Typeset by AFS Image Setters Ltd., Glasgow
Printed and Bound in Great Britain

Cover illustration: 'Destiny' by John William Waterhouse.
The publishers would like to thank Towneley Hall,
Towneley Art Gallery & Museum, Burnley/Bridgeman Art
Library for permission to reproduce this image.

Also available in the *Oxford Literature Resources* series:

Contemporary Stories 1	0 19 831251 2
Contemporary Stories 2	0 19 831254 7
Stories from South Asia	0 19 831255 5
Science Fiction Stories	0 19 831261 X
Fantasy Stories	0 19 831262 8
Sport	0 19 831264 4
Autobiography	0 19 831265 2
Love	0 19 831279 2
Crime Stories	0 19 831280 6
Scottish Short Stories	0 19 831281 4
American Short Stories	0 19 831282 2
Travel Writing	0 19 831283 0
Reportage	0 19 831284 9

Contents

Senses

Reportage

Drama

Acknowledgements

The editor and publisher are grateful for permission to include the following copyright material in this collection.

Nikolai Gogol: extract from *The Government Inspector* (Heinemann Educational Books, 1953), English version by D. J. Campbell, reprinted by permission of Heinemann Publishers Oxford a division of Reed Educational & Professional Publishing Limited. **Thomas Hardy**: 'The Melancholy Hussar of the German Legion' from *Thomas Hardy: Collected Short Stories* (Macmillian, Papermac), reprinted by permission of the publishers. **A. E. Housman**: 'On Wenlock Edge' from *A Shropshire Lad*, reprinted by permission of The Society of Authors as the literary representatives of the Estate of A. E. Housman. **Lucian**: 'No Baggage Allowance' from *Lucian, Satirical Sketches* edited by Betty Radice and Robert Baldick, translated by Paul Turner (Indiana University Press, 1990), reprinted by permission of Paul Turner and Indiana University Press. **Guy de Maupassant**: 'The Necklace', © David Coward 1990, from *A Day in the Country and Other Stories* by Guy de Maupassant translated by David Coward (OUP, 1990) reprinted by permission of Oxford University Press.

Despite every effort it has not been possible to contact every copyright holder prior to publication. If notified, the publisher undertakes to rectify any errors or omissions at the earliest opportunity.

Preface

'Why do we have to read this? It's too old, it's got nothing to do with the way we live now!' Students often make this complaint when they are faced with a text written in another century. Such texts are accused of having other shortcomings: of being too long-winded, too full of difficult words, of portraying characters who simply do not exist any more in our society, and of not dealing with 'real' issues.

Some of these criticisms can be answered by looking at the publicity for the BBC's Short Shakespeare series in which the story-line in *Romeo and Juliet* is described as: 'She's married her boy-friend behind her parents' back. She's smuggled him in under her roof and spent the night with him'. While this description may not do justice to the play, it is designed to overcome many students' reluctance to tackle Shakespeare. It makes the point that although the play is set hundreds of years ago, the situation of the young lovers is still relevant today. The situations and themes of the play are universal, despite the setting. This anthology contains work by writers who, like Shakespeare, are regarded as authors of 'classic works of literature'. Jane Austen, Thomas Hardy, Oliver Goldsmith, and Percy Bysshe Shelley for example, all fall into this category. One of the features which defines them as 'classics', is that they wrote about issues that each succeeding generation recognizes in their own experience. Modern novelists are currently doing this and some of their works will become 'classics' in their turn.

The accusation that old texts do not deal with current issues is refuted in such pieces as Chief Seattle's passionate letter about the need to care for the environment. This seems almost to have been written *before* its time, it is such a clear expression of some current thinking on shrinking natural resources. The poems in the Protest section and Hippolyte Taine's attack on the divide between rich and poor present political issues which are still important today. Media coverage of corruption and sleaze among the rich and powerful have become commonplace in the media; the scenes from Lucian and Gogol show us that there is nothing new in this.

Quick access to information through computers and the speed of electronic communication can make reading seem a slow, cumbersome process. Television and film adaptations of the classics are readily available and very popular. Compared to these, reading some texts in this anthology will require patience and a willingness to persevere. However, some of the texts included are easily accessible; the 'eye-witness' nature of the Letters and Reportage sections make the texts lively and direct. Both sections give examples of personal writing in which the authors reveal their thoughts and feelings about their subjects.

The National Curriculum at Key Stages 3 and 4 requires the study of a variety of forms of writing and the study of texts written before 1900. Many of these forms and some of the authors in the prescribed list feature in this anthology:

- William Shakespeare
- Robert Herrick
- Jane Austen
- Christina Rossetti
- William Blake
- Percy Bysshe Shelley
- Thomas Hardy

Writings from other authors of 'major works of fiction', such as Charles Dickens and George Eliot, are also included. The National Curriculum also requires an 'awareness of the social and historical influences on texts'. It has often been said that 'to know where we are going as a society we need to know where we have come from'. Many of the texts in this anthology give such an insight into the 'progress' made by society.

A full range of spoken and written activities follow on from the texts, together with useful background information for each section. Several of the activities ask you to research the historical context of specific texts in more detail. Other activities place you in the role of certain characters to enable you to gain a deeper insight into the writing.

Another source of pleasure in reading texts from another age comes through the language. At first some elements of the language may appear unfamiliar. Do not let this put you off. The footnotes provided for key words and phrases should help you to get to grips with the text so that you can enjoy the humour and passion which runs through them. Activities have also been devised to help you think about the language and imagery used and to examine the changes in the language shown in some of the texts. With this in mind, original spellings and punctuation have been kept in each piece, showing, amongst other things, that before the Nineteenth Century spelling was not standardized and common nouns were often capitalized. The Jane Austen short story, *The Three Sisters*, which opens the anthology contains the most marked examples of these features.

For those wishing to offer a study of pre-twentieth century texts for coursework the Extended Activities and Wider Reading assignments give plenty of ideas for projects that might be pursued.

Paul Roberts

Short Stories
The Three Sisters

Jane Austen

Miss Stanhope to Mrs——

My dear Fanny

I am the happiest creature in the world, for I have received an offer of marriage from Mr Watts. It is the first I have ever had and I hardly know how to value it enough. How I will triumph over the Duttons! I do not intend to accept it, at least I beleive not, but as I am not quite certain I gave him an equivocal answer and left him. And now my dear Fanny I want your advice whether I should accept his offer or not, but that you may be able to judge of his merits and the situation of affairs I will give you an account of them. He is quite an old man, about two and thirty, very plain, *so* plain that I cannot bear to look at him. He is extremely disagreable and I hate him more than any body else in the world. He has a large fortune and will make great settlements on me; but then he is very healthy. In short I do not know what to do. If I refuse him he as good as told me that he should offer himself to Sophia, and if *she* refused him to Georgiana, and I could not bear to have either of them married before me. If I accept him I know I shall be miserable all the rest of my life, for he is very ill tempered and peevish, extremely jealous, and so stingy that there is no living in the house with him. He told me he should mention the affair to Mama, but I insisted upon it that he did not for very likely she would make me marry him whether I would or no; however probably he *has* before now, for he never does anything he is desired to do. I believe I shall have him. It will be such a triumph to be married before Sophy, Georgiana and the Duttons. And he promised to have a new carriage on the occasion, but we almost quarrelled about the colour, for I insisted upon its being blue spotted with silver, and he declared it should be a plain chocolate; and to provoke me more said it should be just as low as his old one. I wont have him I declare. He said he should come again tomorrow and take my final answer, so I beleive I must get him while I can. I know the Duttons will envy me and I shall be able to chaprone[1] Sophy and Georgiana to all the winter balls. But then what will be the use of that when very likely he wont let me go myself, for I know he hates dancing and what he hates himself he has no idea of any other person's liking: and besides he talks a great deal of

---

[1] *chaprone* – to take on a protective role and escort

women's always staying at home and such stuff. I beleive I shant have him; I would refuse him at once if I were certain that neither of my sisters would accept him, and that if they did not, he would not offer to the Duttons. I cannot run such a risk, so, if he will promise to have the carriage ordered as I like, I will have him, if not he may ride in it by himself for me. I hope you like my determination; I can think of nothing better.

And am your ever affectionate

Mary Stanhope

LETTER 2

Dear Fanny

I had but just sealed my last letter to you when my mother came up and told me she wanted to speak to me on a very particular subject.

'Ah! I know what you mean (said I); that old fool Mr Watts has told you all about it, tho' I bid him not. However you shant force me to have him if I don't like it.'

'I am not going to force you child, but only want to know what your resolution is with regard to his proposals, and to insist upon your making up your mind one way or t'other, that if *you* dont accept him *Sophy* may.'

'Indeed (replied I hastily) Sophy need not trouble herself for I shall certainly marry him myself.'

'If that is your resolution (said my mother) why should you be afraid of my forcing your inclinations?'

'Why, because I have not settled whether I shall have him or not.'

'You are the strangest girl in the world Mary. What you say one moment, you unsay the next. Do tell me once for all, whether you intend to marry Mr Watts or not?'

'Law Mama how can I tell you what I dont know myself?'

'Then I desire you will know, and quickly too, for Mr Watts says he wont be kept in suspense.'

'That depends upon me.'

'No it does not, for if you do not give him your final answer tomorrow when he drinks tea with us, he intends to pay his addresses to Sophy.'

'Then I shall tell all the world that he behaved very ill to me.'

'What good will that do? Mr Watts has been too long abused by all the world to mind it now.'

'I wish I had a father or a brother because then they should fight him.'

'They would be cunning if they did, for Mr Watts would run away first; and therefore you must and shall resolve either to accept or refuse him before tomorrow evening.'

'But why if I don't have him, must he offer to my sisters?'

'Why! because he wishes to be allied to the family and because they are as pretty as you are.'

'But will Sophy marry him Mama if he offers to her?'

'Most likely. Why should not she? If however she does not choose it, then Georgiana must, for I am determined not to let such an opportunity escape of settling one of my daughters so advantageously. So, make the most of your time; I leave you to settle the matter with yourself.' And then she went away. The only thing I can think of my dear Fanny is to ask Sophy and Georgiana whether they would have him were he to make proposals to them, and if they say they would not I am resolved to refuse him too, for I hate him more than you can imagine. As for the Duttons if he marries one of them I shall still have the triumph of having refused him first. So, adeiu[2] my dear friend –

Yours ever *M. S.*

LETTER 3

Miss Georgiana Stanhope to Miss——

Wednesday

My dear Anne

Sophy and I have just been practising a little deceit on our eldest sister, to which we are not perfectly reconciled, and yet the circumstances were such that if any thing will excuse it, they must. Our neighbour Mr Watts has made proposals to Mary: proposals which she knew not how to receive, for tho' she has a particular dislike to him (in which she is not singular) yet she would willingly marry him sooner than risk his offering to Sophy or me which in case of a refusal from herself, he told her he should do, for you must know the poor girl considers our marrying before her as one of the greatest misfortunes that can possibly befall her, and to prevent it would willingly ensure herself everlasting misery by a marriage with Mr Watts. An hour ago she came to us to sound our inclinations respecting the affair which were to determine hers. A little before she came my mother had given us an account of it, telling us that she certainly would not let him go farther than our own family for a wife. 'And therefore (said she) If Mary wont have him Sophy must, and if Sophy wont Georgiana *shall*.' Poor Georgiana! We neither of us attempted to alter my mother's resolution, which I am sorry to say is generally more strictly kept than rationally formed. As soon as she was gone however I broke silence to assure Sophy that if Mary should refuse Mr Watts I should not expect her to sacrifice *her* happiness by becoming his wife from a motive of generosity to me, which I was afraid her good nature and sisterly affection might induce her to do.

'Let us flatter ourselves (replied she) that Mary will not refuse him. Yet

---

[2] *adeiu* – goodbye

how can I hope that my sister may accept a man who cannot make her happy.'

'*He* cannot it is true but his fortune, his name, his house, his carriage will and I have no doubt but that Mary will marry him; indeed why should she not? He is not more than two and thirty; a very proper age for a man to marry at. He is rather plain to be sure, but then what is beauty in a man; if he has but a genteel figure and a sensible looking face it is quite sufficient.'

'This is all very true Georgiana but Mr Watts's figure is unfortunately extremely vulgar and his countenance is very heavy.'

'And then as to his temper; it has been reckoned bad, but may not the world be deceived in their judgement of it. There is an open frankness in his disposition which becomes a man. They say he is stingy; we'll call that prudence. They say he is suspicious. *That* proceeds from a warmth of heart always excusable in youth, and in short I see no reason why he should not make a very good husband, or why Mary should not be very happy with him.'

Sophy laughed; I continued,

'However whether Mary accepts him or not I am resolved. My determination is made. I never would marry Mr Watts were beggary the only alternative. So deficient in every respect! Hideous in his person and without one good quality to make amends for it. His fortune to be sure is good. Yet not so very large! Three thousand a year. What is three thousand a year? It is but six times as much as my mother's income. It will not tempt me.'

'Yet it will be a noble fortune for Mary' said Sophy laughing again.

'For Mary! Yes indeed it will give me pleasure to see *her* in such affluence.'

Thus I ran on to the great entertainment of my sister till Mary came into the room to appearance in great agitation. She sate down. We made room for her at the fire. She seemed at a loss how to begin and at last said in some confusion

'Pray Sophy have you any mind to be married?'

'To be married! None in the least. But why do you ask me? Are you acquainted with any one who means to make me proposals?'

'I – no, how should I? But mayn't I ask a common question?'

'Not a very *common* one Mary surely' (said I). She paused and after some moments silence went on –

'How should you like to marry Mr Watts Sophy?'

I winked at Sophy and replied for her. 'Who is there but must rejoice to marry a man of three thousand a year who keeps a postchaise[3] and pair, with silver harness, a boot before and a window to look out at behind?'

'Very true (she replied), that's very true. So you would have him if he would offer, Georgiana, and would *you* Sophy?'

[3] *postchaise* – an open two-wheeled carriage – also *chaise*

Sophy did not like the idea of telling a lie and deceiving her sister; she prevented the first and saved half her conscience by equivocation.

'I should certainly act just as Georgiana would do.'

'Well then said Mary with triumph in her eyes, *I* have had an offer from Mr Watts.'

We were of course very much surprised: 'Oh! do not accept him said I, and then perhaps he may have me.'

In short my scheme took and Mary is resolved to do *that* to prevent our supposed happiness which she would not have done to ensure it in reality. Yet after all my heart cannot acquit me and Sophy is even more scrupulous. Quiet our minds my dear Anne by writing and telling us you approve our conduct. Consider it well over. Mary will have real pleasure in being a married woman, and able to chaprone us, which she certainly shall do, for I think myself bound to contribute as much as possible to her happiness in a state I have made her choose. They will probably have a new carriage, which will be paradise to her, and if we can prevail on Mr W. to set up his phaeton[4] she will be too happy. These things however would be no consolation to Sophy or me for domestic misery. Remember all this and do not condemn us.

Friday

Last night Mr Watts by appointment drank tea with us. As soon as his carriage stopped at the door, Mary went to the window.

'Would you beleive it Sophy (said she) the old fool wants to have his new chaise[3] just the colour of the old one, and hung as low too. But it shant − I *will* carry my point. And if he wont let it be as high as the Duttons, and blue spotted with silver, I wont have him. Yes I will too. Here he comes. I know he'll be rude; I know he'll be ill-tempered and wont say one civil thing to me! nor behave at all like a lover.' She then sate down and Mr Watts entered.

'Ladies your most obedient.' We paid our compliments and he seated himself.

'Fine weather ladies.' Then turning to Mary, 'Well Miss Stanhope I hope you have *at last* settled the matter in your own mind; and will be so good as to let me know whether you will *condescend* to marry me or not'.

'I think Sir (said Mary) you might have asked in a genteeler way than that. I do not know whether I *shall* have you if you behave so odd.'

'Mary!' (said my mother) 'Well Mama if he will be so cross . . . '

'Hush, hush Mary, you shall not be rude to Mr Watts.'

'Pray Madam do not lay any restraint on Miss Stanhope by obliging her to be civil. If she does not choose to accept my hand, I can offer it else where, for as I am by no means guided by a particular preference to you above your

---

[4] *phaeton* – a light open four-wheeled carriage

sisters it is equally the same to me which I marry of the three.' Was there ever such a wretch! Sophy reddened with anger and I felt *so* spiteful!

'Well then (said Mary in a peevish accent) I *will* have you if I *must*.'

'I should have thought Miss Stanhope that when such settlements are offered as I have offered to you there can be no great violence done to the inclinations in accepting of them.'

Mary mumbled out something, which I who sate close to her could just distinguish to be 'What's the use of a great jointure if men live forever?' And then audibly 'Remember the pinmoney; two hundred a year.'

'A hundred and seventy-five Madam.'

'Two hundred indeed Sir' said my mother.

'And remember I am to have a new carriage hung as high as the Duttons', and blue spotted with silver; and I shall expect a new saddle horse, a suit of fine lace, and an infinite number of the most valuable jewels. Diamonds such as never were seen, pearls as large as those of the Princess Badroulbadour in the 4th volume of the Arabian Nights and rubies, emeralds, toppazes, sapphires, amythists, turkeystones, agate, beads, bugles and garnets and pearls, rubies, emeralds, and beads out of number. You must set up your phaeton which must be cream coloured with a wreath of silver flowers round it, you must buy 4 of the finest bays in the kingdom and you must drive me in it every day. This is not all; you must entirely new furnish your house after my taste, you must hire two more footmen to attend me, two women to wait on me, must always let me do just as I please and make a very good husband.'

Here she stopped, I beleive rather out of breath.

'This is all very reasonable Mr Watts for my daughter to expect.'

'And it is very reasonable Mrs Stanhope that your daughter should be disappointed.' He was going on but Mary interrupted him. 'You must build me an elegant greenhouse and stock it with plants. You must let me spend every winter in Bath, every spring in Town[5], every summer in taking some tour, and every autumn at a watering place,[6] and if we are at home the rest of the year (Sophy and I laughed) you must do nothing but give balls and masquerades. You must build a room on purpose and a theatre to act plays in. The first play we have shall be *Which is the Man*, and I will do Lady Bell Bloomer.'

'And pray Miss Stanhope (said Mr Watts) What am I to expect from you in return for all this.'

'Expect? why you may expect to have me pleased.'

'It would be odd if I did not. Your expectations Madam are too high for me, and I must apply to Miss Sophy who perhaps may not have raised her's so much.'

---

[5] *Town* – London

[6] *a watering place* – either a spa town like Bath or a sea-bathing place like Weymouth

'You are mistaken Sir in supposing so, (said Sophy) for tho' they may not be exactly in the same line, yet my expectations are to the full as high as my sister's; for I expect my husband to be good tempered and chearful; to consult my happiness in all his actions, and to love me with constancy and sincerity.'

Mr Watts stared. 'These are very odd ideas truly young lady. You had better discard them before you marry, or you will be obliged to do it afterwards.'

My mother in the meantime was lecturing Mary who was sensible that she had gone too far, and when Mr Watts was just turning towards me in order I beleive to address me, she spoke to him in a voice half humble, half sulky.

'You are mistaken Mr Watts if you think I was earnest when I said I expected so much. However I must have a new chaise.'

'Yes Sir you must allow that Mary has a right to expect that.'

'Mrs Stanhope, I *mean* and have always meant to have a new one on my marriage. But it shall be the colour of my present one.'

'I think Mr Watts you should pay my girl the compliment of consulting her taste on such matters.'

Mr Watts would not agree to this, and for some time insisted upon its being a chocolate colour, while Mary was as eager for having it blue with silver spots. At length however Sophy proposed that to please Mr W. it should be a dark brown and to please Mary it should be hung rather high and have a silver border. This was at length agreed to, tho' reluctantly on both sides, as each had intended to carry their point entire. We then proceeded to other matters, and it was settled that they should be married as soon as the writings could be completed. Mary was very eager for a special licence[7] and Mr Watts talked of banns. A common licence was at last agreed on. Mary is to have all the family jewels which are very inconsiderable I beleive and Mr W. promised to buy her a saddle horse; but in return she is not to expect to go to Town or any other public place for these three years. She is to have neither greenhouse, theatre or phaeton; to be contented with one maid without an additional footman. It engrossed the whole evening to settle these affairs; Mr W. supped with us and did not go till twelve. As soon as he was gone Mary exclaimed. 'Thank Heaven! he's off at last; how I do hate him!' It was in vain that Mama represented to her the impropriety she was guilty of in disliking him who was to be her husband, for she persisted in declaring her aversion to him and hoping she might never see him again. What a wedding will this be! Adeiu my dear Anne. Your faithfully sincere

Georgiana Stanhope

[7] *a special licence* – a licence was needed before the marriage ceremony. The period of delay between obtaining the licence and being married could be shortened by a special licence

LETTER 4

The same to the same

Saturday

Dear Anne

Mary eager to have every one know of her approaching wedding and more particularly desirous of triumphing as she called it over the Duttons, desired us to walk with her this morning to Stoneham. As we had nothing else to do we readily agreed, and had as pleasant a walk as we could have with Mary whose conversation entirely consisted in abusing the man she is so soon to marry and in longing for a blue chaise spotted with silver. When we reached the Duttons we found the two girls in the dressing-room with a very handsome young man, who was of course introduced to us. He is the son of Sir Henry Brudenell of Leicestershire – Mr Brudenell is the handsomest man I ever saw in my life; we are all three very much pleased with him. Mary, who from the moment of our reaching the dressing-room had been swelling with the knowledge of her own importance and with the desire of making it known, could not remain long silent on the subject after we were seated, and soon addressing herself to Kitty said,

'Dont you think it will be necessary to have all the jewels new set?'

'Necessary for what?'

'For what! Why for my appearance.'

'I beg your pardon but I really do not understand you. What jewels do you speak of, and where is your appearance to be made?'

'At the next ball to be sure after I am married.'

You may imagine their surprise. They were at first incredulous, but on our joining in the story they at last beleived it. 'And who is it to' was of course the first question. Mary pretended bashfulness, and answered in confusion her eyes cast down 'to Mr Watts'. This also required confirmation from us, for that anyone who had the beauty and fortune (tho' small yet a provision) of Mary would willingly marry Mr Watts, could by them scarcely be credited. The subject being now fairly introduced and she found herself the object of every one's attention in company, she lost all her confusion and became perfectly unreserved and communicative.

'I wonder you should never have heard of it before for in general things of this nature are very well known in the neighbourhood.'

'I assure you said Jemima I never had the least suspicion of such an affair. Has it been in agitation long?'

'Oh! Yes, ever since Wednesday.'

They all smiled particularly Mr Brudenell.

'You must know Mr Watts is very much in love with me, so that it is quite a match of affection on his side.'

'Not on his only, I suppose' said Kitty.

'Oh! when there is so much love on one side there is no occasion for it on the other. However I do not much dislike him tho' he is very plain to be sure.'

Mr Brudenell stared, the Miss Duttons laughed and Sophy and I were heartily ashamed of our sister. She went on.

'We are to have a new postchaise and very likely may set up our phaeton.'

This we knew to be false but the poor girl was pleased at the idea of persuading the company that such a thing was to be and I would not deprive her of so harmless an enjoyment. She continued.

'Mr Watts is to present me with the family jewels which I fancy are very considerable.' I could not help whispering Sophy 'I fancy not'. 'These jewels are what I suppose must be new set before they can be worn. I shall not wear them till the first ball I go to after my marriage. If Mrs Dutton should not go to it, I hope you will let me chaprone you; I shall certainly take Sophy and Georgiana.'

'You are very good (said Kitty) and since you are inclined to undertake the care of young ladies, I should advise you to prevail on Mrs Edgecumbe to let you chaprone her six daughters which with your two sisters and ourselves will make your entrée very respectable.'

Kitty made us all smile except Mary who did not understand her meaning and coolly said that she should not like to chaprone so many. Sophy and I now endeavoured to change the conversation but succeeded only for a few minutes, for Mary took care to bring back their attention to her and her approaching wedding. I was sorry for my sister's sake to see that Mr Brudenell seemed to take pleasure in listening to her account of it and even encouraged her by his questions and remarks, for it was evident that his only aim was to laugh at her. I am afraid he found her very ridiculous. He kept his countenance extremely well, yet it was easy to see that it was with difficulty he kept it. At length however he seemed fatigued and disgusted with her ridiculous conversation, as he turned from her to us, and spoke but little to her for about half an hour before we left Stoneham. As soon as we were out of the house we all joined in praising the person and manners of Mr Brudenell.

We found Mr Watts at home.

'So, Miss Stanhope (said he) you see I am come a courting in a true lover like manner.'

'Well you need not have *told* me that. I knew why you came very well.'

Sophy and I then left the room, imagining of course that we must be in the way, if a scene of courtship were to begin. We were surprised at being followed almost immediately by Mary.

'And is your courting so soon over?' said Sophy.

'Courting! (replied Mary) we have been quarrelling. Watts is such a fool! I hope I shall never see him again.'

'I am afraid you will, (said I) as he dines here today. But what has been your dispute?'

'Why only because I told him that I had seen a man much handsomer than he was this morning, he flew into a great passion and called me a vixen, so I only stayed to tell him I thought him a blackguard[8] and came away.'

'Short and sweet; (said Sophy) but pray Mary how will this be made up?'

'He ought to ask my pardon; but if he did, I would not forgive him.'

'His submission then would not be very useful.'

When we were dressed we returned to the parlour where Mama and Mr Watts were in close conversation. It seems that he had been complaining to her of her daughter's behaviour, and she had persuaded him to think no more of it. He therefore met Mary with all his accustomed civility, and except one touch at the phaeton and another at the greenhouse, the evening went off with great harmony and cordiality. Watts is going to Town to hasten the preparations for the wedding.

I am your affectionate friend *G.S*

[8] *blackguard* – a badly behaved person

The Necklace

Guy de Maupassant

She was one of those pretty, delightful girls who, apparently by some error of Fate, get themselves born the daughters of very minor civil servants. She had no dowry, no expectations, no means of meeting some rich, important man who would understand, love, and marry her. So she went along with a proposal made by a junior clerk in the Ministry of Education.

She dressed simply, being unable to afford anything better, but she was every whit as unhappy as any daughter of good family who has come down in the world. Women have neither rank nor class, and their beauty, grace, and charm do service for birthright and connections. Natural guile, instinctive elegance, and adaptability are what determines their place in the hierarchy, and a girl of no birth to speak of may easily be the equal of any society lady.

She was unhappy all the time, for she felt that she was intended for a life of refinement and luxury. She was made unhappy by the run-down apartment they lived in, the peeling walls, the battered chairs, and the ugly curtains. Now all this, which any other woman of her station might never even have noticed, was torture to her and made her very angry. The spectacle of the young Breton[1] peasant girl who did the household chores stirred sad regrets and impossible fancies. She dreamed of silent antechambers hung with oriental tapestries, lit by tall, bronze candelabras, and of two tall footmen in liveried breeches asleep in the huge armchairs, dozing in the heavy heat of a stove. She dreamed of great drawing-rooms dressed with old silk, filled with fine furniture which showed off trinkets beyond price, and of pretty little parlours, filled with perfumes and just made for intimate talk at five in the afternoon with one's closest friends who would be the most famous and sought-after men of the day whose attentions were much coveted and desired by all women.

When she sat down to dinner at the round table spread with a three-day-old cloth, facing her husband who always lifted the lid of the soup-tureen and declared delightedly: 'Ah! Stew! Splendid! There's nothing I like better than a nice stew . . . ', she dreamed of elegant dinners, gleaming silverware, and tapestries which peopled the walls with mythical characters and strange birds in enchanted forests; she dreamed of exquisite dishes served on fabulous china plates, of pretty compliments whispered into willing ears and received with Sphinx-like smiles over the pink flesh of a trout or the wings of a hazel hen.

---

[1] *Breton* – from Brittany in Northern France

She had no fine dresses, no jewellery, nothing. And that was all she cared about; she felt that God had made her for such things. She would have given anything to be popular, envied, attractive, and in demand.

She had a friend who was rich, a friend from her convent days, on whom she never called now, for she was always so unhappy afterwards. Sometimes, for days on end, she would weep tears of sorrow, regret, despair, and anguish.

One evening her husband came home looking highly pleased with himself. In his hand he brandished a large envelope.

'Look,' he said, 'I've got something for you.'

She tore the paper flap eagerly and extracted a printed card bearing these words:

'The Minister of Education and Madame Georges Ramponneau request the pleasure of the company of Monsieur and Madame Loisel at the Ministry Buildings on the evening of 18 January.'

Instead of being delighted as her husband had hoped, she tossed the invitation peevishly onto the table and muttered: 'What earthly use is that to me?'

'But, darling, I thought you'd be happy. You never go anywhere and it's an opportunity, a splendid opportunity! I had the dickens of job getting hold of an invite. Everybody's after them; they're very much in demand and not many are handed out to us clerks. You'll be able to see all the big nobs there.'

She looked at him irritably and said shortly: 'And what am I supposed to wear if I do go?'

He had not thought of that. He blustered: 'What about the dress you wear for the theatre? It looks all right to me . . . ' The words died in his throat. He was totally disconcerted and dismayed by the sight of his wife who had begun to cry. Two large tears rolled slowly out of the corners of her eyes and down towards the sides of her mouth.

'What's up?' he stammered. 'What's the matter?'

Making a supreme effort, she controlled her sorrows and, wiping her damp cheeks, replied quite calmly: 'Nothing. It's just that I haven't got anything to wear and consequently I shan't be going to any reception. Give the invite to one of your colleagues with a wife who is better off for clothes than I am.'

He was devastated. He went on: 'Oh come on, Mathilde. Look, what could it cost to get something suitable that would do for other occasions, something fairly simple?'

She thought for a few moments, working out her sums but also wondering how much she could decently ask for without drawing an immediate refusal and pained protests from her husband who was careful with his money.

Finally, after some hesitation, she said: 'I can't say precisely, but I daresay I could get by on four hundred francs.'

He turned slightly pale, for he had been setting aside just that amount to buy a gun and finance hunting trips the following summer in the flat landscape around Nanterre[2] with a few friends who went shooting larks there on Sundays. But he said: 'Very well. I'll give you your four hundred francs. But do try and get a decent dress.'

The day of the reception drew near and Madame Loisel appeared sad, worried, anxious. Yet all her clothes were ready. One evening her husband said: 'What's up? You haven't half been acting funny these last few days.'

She replied: 'It vexes me that I haven't got a single piece of jewellery, not one stone, that I can put on. I'll look like a church mouse. I'd almost as soon not go to the reception.'

'Wear a posy,' he said.' 'It's all the rage this year. You could get two or three magnificent roses for ten francs.'

She was not convinced. 'No. . . . There's nothing so humiliating as to look poor when you're with women who are rich.'

But her husband exclaimed: 'You aren't half silly! Look, go and see your friend, Madame Forestier, and ask her to lend you some jewellery. You know her well enough for that.'

She gave a delighted cry: 'You're right! I never thought of that!'

The next day she called on her friend and told her all about her problem. Madame Forestier went over to a mirror-fronted wardrobe, took out a large casket, brought it over, unlocked it, and said to Madame Loisel: 'Choose whatever you like.'

At first she saw bracelets, then a rope of pearls and a Venetian cross made of gold and diamonds admirably fashioned. She tried on the necklaces in the mirror, and could hardly bear to take them off and give them back. She kept asking: 'Have you got anything else?'

'Yes, of course. Just look. I can't say what sort of thing you'll like best.'

All of sudden, in a black satinwood case, she found a magnificent diamond necklace, and her heart began to beat with immoderate desire. Her hand shook as she picked it up. She fastened it around her throat over her high-necked dress and sat looking at herself in rapture. Then, diffidently, apprehensively, she asked: 'Can you lend me this? Nothing else. Just this.'

'But of course.'

She threw her arms around her friend, kissed her extravagantly, and then ran home, taking her treasure with her.

---

[2] *Nanterre* – a rural area near Paris

The day of the reception arrived. Madame Loisel was a success. She was the prettiest woman there, elegant, graceful, radiant, and wonderfully happy. All the men looked at her, enquired who she was, and asked to be introduced. All the cabinet secretaries and under-secretaries wanted to waltz with her. She was even noticed by the Minister himself.

She danced ecstatically, wildly, intoxicated with pleasure, giving no thought to anything else, swept along on her victorious beauty and glorious success, and floating on a cloud of happiness composed of the homage, admiration, and desire she evoked and the kind of complete and utter triumph which is so sweet to a woman's heart.

She left at about four in the morning. Since midnight her husband had been dozing in a small, empty side-room with three other men whose wives were having an enjoyable time.

He helped her on with her coat which he had fetched when it was time to go, a modest, everyday coat, a commonplace coat violently at odds with the elegance of her dress. It brought her down to earth, and she would have preferred to slip away quietly and avoid being noticed by the other women who were being arrayed in rich furs. But Loisel grabbed her by the arm: 'Wait a sec. You'll catch cold outside. I'll go and get a cab.'

But she refused to listen and ran quickly down the stairs. When they were outside in the street, there was no cab in sight. They began looking for one, hailing all the cabbies they saw driving by in the distance.

They walked down to the Seine[3] in desperation, shivering with cold. There, on the embankment, they at last found one of those aged nocturnal hackney cabs which only emerge in Paris after dusk, as if ashamed to parade their poverty in the full light of day. It bore them back to their front door in the rue des Martyrs, and they walked sadly up to their apartment. For her it was all over, while he was thinking that he would have to be at the Ministry at ten.

Standing in front of the mirror, she took off the coat she had been wearing over her shoulders, to get a last look at herself in all her glory. Suddenly she gave a cry. The necklace was no longer round her throat!

Her husband, who was already half undressed, asked: 'What's up?'

She turned to him in a panic: 'I . . . I . . . Madame Forestier's necklace . . . I haven't got it!'

He straightened up as if thunderstruck: 'What? . . . But . . . You can't have lost it!'

They looked in the pleats of her dress, in the folds of her coat, and in her pockets. They looked everywhere. They did not find it.

'Are you sure you still had it when you left the ballroom? he asked.

---

[3] *Seine* – the river running through Paris

'Yes, I remember fingering it in the entrance hall.'

'But if you'd lost it in the street, we'd have heard it fall. So it must be in the cab.'

'That's right. That's probably it. Did you get his number?'

'No. Did you happen to notice it?'

'No.'

They looked at each other in dismay. Finally Loisel got dressed again. 'I'm going to go back the way we came,' he said, 'to see if I can find it.' He went out. She remained as she was, still wearing her evening gown, not having the strength to go to bed, sitting disconsolately on a chair by the empty grate, her mind a blank.

Her husband returned at about seven o'clock. He had found nothing.

He went to the police station, called at newspaper offices where he advertised a reward, toured the cab companies, and tried anywhere where the faintest of hopes led him. She waited for him all day long in the same distracted condition, thinking of the appalling catastrophe which had befallen them.

Loisel came back that evening, hollow-cheeked and very pale. He had not come up with anything.

'Look,' he said, 'you'll have to write to your friend and say you broke the catch on her necklace and you are getting it repaired. That'll give us time to work out what we'll have to do.'

She wrote to his dictation.

A week later they had lost all hope.

Loisel, who had aged five years, said: 'We'll have to start thinking about replacing the necklace.'

The next day they took the case in which it had come and called on the jeweller whose name was inside. He looked through his order book.

'It wasn't me that sold the actual necklace. I only supplied the case.'

After this, they trailed round jeweller's shops, looking for a necklace just like the other one, trying to remember it, and both ill with worry and anxiety.

In a shop in the Palais Royal they found a diamond collar which they thought was identical to the one they were looking for. It cost forty thousand francs. The jeweller was prepared to let them have it for thirty-six.

They asked him not to sell it for three days. And they got him to agree to take it back for thirty-four thousand if the one that had been lost turned up before the end of February.

Loisel had eighteen thousand francs which his father had left him. He would have to borrow the rest.

He borrowed the money, a thousand francs here, five hundred there, sometimes a hundred and as little as sixty. He signed notes, agreed to pay exorbitant rates of interest, resorted to usurers and the whole tribe of moneylenders. He mortgaged the rest of his life, signed papers without knowing if he would ever be able to honour his commitments, and then, sick with worry about the future, the grim poverty which stood ready to pounce, and the prospect of all the physical privation and mental torture ahead, he went round to the jeweller's to get the new necklace with the thirty-six thousand francs which he put on the counter.

When Madame Loisel took it round, Madame Forestier said in a huff: 'You ought really to have brought it back sooner. I might have needed it.'

She did not open the case, as her friend had feared she might. If she had noticed the substitution, what would she have thought? What would she have said? Would she not have concluded she was a thief?

Then began for Madame Loisel the grindingly horrible life of the very poor. But quickly and heroically, she resigned herself to what she could not alter: their appalling debt would have to be repaid. She was determined to pay. They dismissed the maid. They moved out of their apartment and rented an attic room.

She became used to heavy domestic work and all kinds of ghastly kitchen chores. She washed dishes, wearing down her pink nails on the greasy pots and saucepans. She washed the dirty sheets, shirts, and floorcloths by hand and hung them up to dry on a line; each morning she took the rubbish down to the street and carried the water up, pausing for breath on each landing. And, dressed like any working-class woman, she shopped at the fruiterer's, the grocer's, and the butcher's, with a basket over her arm, haggling, frequently abused and always counting every penny.

Each month they had to settle some accounts, renew others, and bargain for time.

Her husband worked in the evenings doing accounts for a shopkeeper and quite frequently sat up into the early hours doing copying work at five sous a page.

They lived like this for ten years.

By the time ten years had gone by, they had repaid everything, with not a penny outstanding, in spite of the extortionate conditions and including the accumulated interest.

Madame Loisel looked old now. She had turned into the battling, hard, uncouth housewife who rules working-class homes. Her hair was untidy, her skirts were askew, and her hands were red. She spoke in a gruff voice and scrubbed floors on her hands and knees. But sometimes, when her husband had gone to the office, she would sit by the window and think of that evening long ago when she had been so beautiful and so admired.

What might not have happened had she not lost the necklace? Who could tell? Who could possibly tell? Life is so strange, so fickle! How little is needed to make or break us!

One Sunday, needing a break from her heavy working week, she went out for a stroll on the Champs-Elysées. Suddenly she caught sight of a woman pushing a child in a pram. It was Madame Forestier, still young, still beautiful, and still attractive.

Madame Loisel felt apprehensive. Should she speak to her? Yes, why not? Now that she had paid in full, she would tell her everything. Why not? She went up to her.

'Hello, Jeanne.'

The friend did not recognize her and was taken aback at being addressed so familiarly by a common woman in the street. She stammered: 'But . . . I'm sorry . . . I don't know . . . There's some mistake.'

'No mistake. I'm Mathilde Loisel.'

Her friend gave a cry: 'But my poor Mathilde, how you've changed!'

'Yes, I've been through some hard times since I saw you, very hard times. And it was all on your account.'

'On my account? Whatever do you mean?'

'Do you remember that diamond necklace you lent me to go to the reception at the Ministry?'

'Yes. What about it?'

'Well I lost it.'

'Lost it? But you returned it to me.'

'No, I returned another one just like it. And we've been paying for it these past ten years. You know, it wasn't easy for us. We had nothing . . . But it's over and done with now, and I'm glad.'

Madame Forestier stopped. 'You mean you bought a diamond necklace to replace mine?'

'Yes. And you never noticed the difference, did you? They were exactly alike.' And she smiled a proud, innocent smile.

Madame Forestier looked very upset and, taking both her hands in hers, said:

'Oh, my poor Mathilde! But it was only an imitation necklace. It couldn't have been worth much more than five hundred francs! . . .'

The Melancholy Hussar of the German Legion

Thomas Hardy

I

Here stretch the downs; high and breezy and green, absolutely unchanged since those eventful days. A plough has never disturbed the turf, and the sod that was uppermost then is uppermost now. Here stood the camp; here are distinct traces of the banks thrown up for the horses of the cavalry, and spots where the midden-heaps lay are still to be observed. At night, when I walk across the lonely place, it is impossible to avoid hearing, amid the scourings of the wind over the grass-bents and thistles, the old trumpet and bugle calls, the rattle of the halters; to help seeing rows of spectral tents and the *impedimenta*[1] of the soldiery. From within the canvases come guttural syllables of foreign tongues, and broken songs of the fatherland; for they were mainly regiments of the King's German Legion[2] that slept round the tent-poles hereabout at that time.

It was nearly ninety years ago. The British uniform of the period, with its immense epaulettes, queer cocked-hat, breeches, gaiters, ponderous cartridge-box, buckled shoes, and what not, would look strange and barbarous now. Ideas have changed; invention has followed invention. Soldiers were monumental objects then. A divinity still hedged kings here and there; and war was considered a glorious thing.

Secluded old manor-houses and hamlets lie in the ravines and hollows among these hills, where a stranger had hardly ever been seen till the King chose to take the baths[3] yearly at the sea-side watering-place a few miles to the south; as a consequence of which battalions descended in a cloud upon the open country around. Is it necessary to add that the echoes of many characteristic tales, dating from that picturesque time, still linger about here in more or less fragmentary form, to be caught by the attentive ear? Some of them I have repeated; most of them I have forgotten; one I have never repeated, and assuredly can never forget.

---

[1] impedimenta – equipment
[2] *King's German Legion* – George III of England was also the King of Germany and the legion came from Germany
[3] *to take the baths* – sea-bathing became popular at the time of George III when this story takes place. The town referred to here is Weymouth.

Phyllis told me the story with her own lips. She was then an old lady of seventy-five, and her auditor a lad of fifteen. She enjoined silence as to her share of the incident, till she should be 'dead, buried, and forgotten'. Her life was prolonged twelve years after the day of her narration, and she has now been dead nearly twenty. The oblivion which in her modesty and humility she courted for herself has only partially fallen on her, with the unfortunate result of inflicting an injustice upon her memory; since such fragments of her story as got abroad at the time, and have been kept alive ever since, are precisely those which are most unfavourable to her character.

It all began with the arrival of the York Hussars,[4] one of the foreign regiments above alluded to. Before that day scarcely a soul had been seen near her father's house for weeks. When a noise like the brushing skirt of a visitor was heard on the doorstep, it proved to be a scudding leaf; when a carriage seemed to be nearing the door, it was her father grinding his sickle on the stone in the garden for his favourite relaxation of trimming the box-tree borders to the plots. A sound like luggage thrown down from the coach was a gun far away at sea; and what looked like a tall man by the gate at dusk was a yew bush cut into a quaint and attenuated shape. There is no such solitude in country places now as there was in those old days.

Yet all the while King George and his court were at his favourite sea-side resort, not more than five miles off.

The daughter's seclusion was great, but beyond the seclusion of the girl lay the seclusion of the father. If her social condition was twilight, his was darkness. Yet he enjoyed his darkness, while her twilight oppressed her. Dr Grove had been a professional man whose taste for lonely meditation over metaphysical questions had diminished his practice till it no longer paid him to keep it going; after which he had relinquished it and hired at a nominal rent the small, dilapidated, half farm half manorhouse of this obscure inland nook, to make a sufficiency of an income which in a town would have been inadequate for their maintenance. He stayed in his garden the greater part of the day, growing more and more irritable with the lapse of time, and the increasing perception that he had wasted his life in the pursuit of illusions. He saw his friends less and less frequently. Phyllis became so shy that if she met a stranger anywhere in her short rambles she felt ashamed at his gaze, walked awkwardly, and blushed to her shoulders.

Yet Phyllis was discovered even here by an admirer, and her hand most unexpectedly asked in marriage.

The King, as aforesaid, was at the neighbouring town, where he had taken up his abode at Gloucester Lodge; and his presence in the town naturally brought many county people thither. Among these idlers – many of whom

[4] *York Hussars* – a cavalry regiment

professed to have connections and interests with the Court – was one Humphrey Gould, a bachelor; a personage neither young nor old; neither good-looking nor positively plain. Too steady-going to be 'a buck' (as fast and unmarried men were then called), he was an approximately fashionable man of a mild type. This bachelor of thirty found his way to the village on the down: beheld Phyllis; made her father's acquaintance in order to make hers; and by some means or other she sufficiently inflamed his heart to lead him in that direction almost daily; till he became engaged to marry her.

As he was of an old local family, some of whose members were held in respect in the county, Phyllis, in bringing him to her feet, had accomplished what was considered a brilliant move for one in her constrained position. How she had done it was not quite known to Phyllis herself. In those days unequal marriages were regarded rather as a violation of the laws of nature than as a mere infringement of convention, the more modern view, and hence when Phyllis, of the watering-place *bourgeoisie*,[5] was chosen by such a gentlemanly[6] fellow, it was as if she were going to be taken to heaven, though perhaps the uninformed would have seen no great difference in the respective positions of the pair, the said Gould being as poor as a crow.

This pecuniary condition was his excuse – probably a true one – for postponing their union, and as the winter drew nearer, and the King departed for the season, Mr Humphrey Gould set out for Bath, promising to return to Phyllis in a few weeks. The winter arrived, the date of his promise passed, yet Gould postponed his coming, on the ground that he could not very easily leave his father in the city of their sojourn, the elder having no other relative near him. Phyllis, though lonely in the extreme, was content. The man who had asked her in marriage was a desirable husband for her in many ways; her father highly approved of his suit; but this neglect of her was awkward, if not painful, for Phyllis. Love him in the true sense of the word she assured me she never did, but she had a genuine regard for him; admired a certain methodical and dogged way in which he sometimes took his pleasure; valued his knowledge of what the Court was doing, had done, or was about to do; and she was not without a feeling of pride that he had chosen her when he might have exercised a more ambitious choice.

But he did not come; and the spring developed. His letters were regular though formal; and it is not to be wondered that the uncertainty of her position, linked with the fact that there was not much passion in her thoughts of Humphrey, bred an indescribable dreariness in the heart of Phyllis Grove. The spring was soon summer, and the summer brought the King; but still no

---

[5] bourgeoisie – the middle classes
[6] *gentlemanly* – of the upper classes

Humphrey Gould. All this while the engagement by letter was maintained intact.

At this point of time a golden radiance flashed in upon the lives of people here, and charged all youthful thought with emotional interest. This radiance was the aforesaid York Hussars.

II

The present generation has probably but a very dim notion of the celebrated York Hussars of ninety years ago. They were one of the regiments of the King's German Legion, and (though they somewhat degenerated later on) their brilliant uniform, their splendid horses, and above all, their foreign air and mustachios (rare appendages then), drew crowds of admirers of both sexes wherever they went. These with other regiments had come to encamp on the downs and pastures, because of the presence of the King in the neighbouring town.

The spot was high and airy, and the view extensive, commanding Portland – the Isle of Slingers – in front, and reaching to St Aldhelm's Head eastward, and almost to the Start on the west.

Phyllis, though not precisely a girl of the village, was as interested as any of them in this military investment. Her father's home stood somewhat apart, and on the highest point of ground to which the lane ascended, so that it was almost level with the top of the church tower in the lower part of the parish. Immediately from the outside of the garden-wall the grass spread away to a great distance, and it was crossed by a path which came close to the wall. Ever since her childhood it had been Phyllis's pleasure to clamber up this fence and sit on the top – a feat not so difficult as it may seem, the walls in this district being built of rubble, without mortar, so that there were plenty of crevices for small toes.

She was sitting up here one day, listlessly surveying the pasture without, when her attention was arrested by a solitary figure walking along the path. It was one of the renowned German Hussars, and he moved onward with his eyes on the ground, and with the manner of one who wished to escape company. His head would probably have been bent like his eyes but for his stiff neck-gear. On nearer view she perceived that his face was marked with deep sadness. Without observing her, he advanced by the footpath till it brought him almost immediately under the wall.

Phyllis was much surprised to see a fine, tall soldier in such a mood as this. Her theory of the military, and of the York Hussars in particular (derived entirely from hearsay, for she had never talked to a soldier in her life), was that their hearts were as gay as their accoutrements.

At this moment the Hussar lifted his eyes and noticed her on her perch, the white muslin neckerchief which covered her shoulders and neck where left bare by her low gown, and her white raiment in general, showing conspicuously in the bright sunlight of this summer day. He blushed a little at the suddenness of the encounter, and without halting a moment from his pace passed on.

All that day the foreigner's face haunted Phyllis; its aspect was so striking, so handsome, and his eyes were so blue, and sad, and abstracted. It was perhaps only natural that on some following day at the same hour she should look over that wall again, and wait till he had passed a second time. On this occasion he was reading a letter, and at the sight of her his manner was that of one who had half expected or hoped to discover her. He almost stopped, smiled, and made a courteous salute. The end of the meeting was that they exchanged a few words. She asked him what he was reading, and he readily informed her that he was re-perusing letters from his mother in Germany; he did not get them often, he said, and was forced to read the old ones a great many times. This was all that passed at the present interview, but others of the same kind followed.

Phyllis used to say that his English, though not good, was quite intelligible to her, so that their acquaintance was never hindered by difficulties of speech. Whenever the subject became too delicate, subtle, or tender, for such words of English as were at his command, the eyes no doubt helped out the tongue, and – though this was later on – the lips helped out the eyes. In short this acquaintance, unguardedly made, and rash enough on her part, developed and ripened. Like Desdemona, she pitied him, and learnt his history.[7]

His name was Matthäus Tina, and Saarbrück[8] his native town, where his mother was still living. His age was twenty-two, and he had already risen to the grade of corporal, though he had not long been in the army. Phyllis used to assert that no such refined or well-educated young man could have been found in the ranks of the purely English regiments, some of these foreign soldiers having rather the graceful manner and presence of our native officers than of our rank and file.

She by degrees learnt from her foreign friend a circumstance about himself and his comrades which Phyllis would least have expected of the York Hussars. So far from being as gay as its uniform, the regiment was pervaded by a dreadful melancholy, a chronic home-sickness, which depressed many of the men to such an extent that they could hardly attend to their drill. The worst sufferers were the younger soldiers who had not been over here long. They hated England and English life; they took no interest whatever in King

---

[7] *Like Desdemona . . . his history* – In Shakespeare's *Othello* Desdemona listens to Othello's stories of adventure and falls in love with him.

[8] *Saarbrück* – a German town on the border with France

George and his island kingdom, and they only wished to be out of it and never to see it any more. Their bodies were here, but their hearts and minds were always far away in their dear fatherland, of which – brave men and stoical as they were in many ways – they would speak with tears in their eyes. One of the worst of the sufferers from this home-woe, as he called it in his own tongue, was Matthäus Tina, whose dreamy musing nature felt the gloom of exile still more intensely from the fact that he had left a lonely mother at home with nobody to cheer her.

Though Phyllis, touched by all this, and interested in his history, did not disdain her soldier's acquaintance, she declined (according to her own account, at least) to permit the young man to overstep the line of mere friendship for a long while – as long, indeed, as she considered herself likely to become the possession of another; though it is probable that she had lost her heart to Matthäus before she was herself aware. The stone wall of necessity made anything like intimacy difficult; and he had never ventured to come, or to ask to come, inside the garden, so that all their conversation had been overtly conducted across this boundary.

III

But news reached the village from a friend of Phyllis's father concerning Mr Humphrey Gould, her remarkably cool and patient betrothed. This gentleman had been heard to say in Bath that he considered his overtures to Miss Phyllis Grove to have reached only the stage of a half-understanding; and in view of his enforced absence on his father's account, who was too great an invalid now to attend to his affairs, he thought it best that there should be no definite promise as yet on either side. He was not sure, indeed, that he might not cast his eyes elsewhere.

This account – though only a piece of hearsay, and as such entitled to no absolute credit – tallied so well with the infrequency of his letters and their lack of warmth, that Phyllis did not doubt its truth for one moment; and from that hour she felt herself free to bestow her heart as she should choose. Not so her father; he declared the whole story to be a fabrication. He had known Mr Gould's family from his boyhood; and if there was one proverb which expressed the matrimonial aspect of that family well, it was 'Love me little, love me long.' Humphrey was an honourable man, who would not think of treating his engagement so lightly. 'Do you wait in patience,' he said; 'all will be right in time.'

From these words Phyllis at first imagined that her father was in correspondence with Mr Gould; and her heart sank within her; for in spite of her original intentions she had been relieved to hear that her engagement had come to nothing. But she presently learnt that her father had heard no more of Humphrey Gould than she herself had done; while he would not write and address her affianced directly on the subject, lest it should be deemed an imputation on that bachelor's honour.

'You want an excuse for encouraging one or other of those foreign fellows to flatter you with his unmeaning attentions, her father exclaimed, his mood having of late been a very unkind one towards her. 'I see more than I say. Don't you ever set foot outside that garden-fence without my permission. If you want to see that camp I'll take you myself some Sunday afternoon.'

Phyllis had not the smallest intention of disobeying him in her actions, but she assumed herself to be independent with respect to her feelings. She no longer checked her fancy for the Hussar, though she was far from regarding him as her lover in the serious sense in which an Englishman might have been regarded as such. The young foreign soldier was almost an ideal being to her, with none of the appurtenances of an ordinary house-dweller; one who had descended she knew not whence, and would disappear she knew not whither; the subject of a fascinating dream – no more.

They met continually now – mostly at dusk – during the brief interval between the going down of the sun and the minute at which the last trumpet-call summoned him to his tent. Perhaps her manner had become less restrained latterly; at any rate that of the Hussar was so; he had grown more tender every day, and at parting after these hurried interviews she reached down her hand from the top of the wall that he might press it. One evening he held it such a while that she exclaimed, 'The wall is white, and somebody in the field may see your shape against it!'

He lingered so long that night that it was with the greatest difficulty that he could run across the intervening stretch of ground and enter the camp in time. On the next occasion of his awaiting her she did not appear in her usual place at the usual hour. His disappointment was unspeakably keen; he remained staring blankly at the spot, like a man in a trance. The trumpets and tattoo[9] sounded, and still he did not go.

She had been delayed purely by an accident. When she arrived she was anxious because of the lateness of the hour, having heard as well as he the sounds denoting the closing of the camp. She implored him to leave immediately.

'No,' he said gloomily. 'I shall not go in yet – the moment you come – I have thought of your coming all day.'

'But you may be disgraced at being after time?'

'I don't mind that. I should have disappeared from the world some time ago if it had not been for two persons – my beloved, here, and my mother

---

[9] *tattoo* – the bugle call recalling soldiers to camp at the end of the day.

in Saarbrück. I hate the army. I care more for a minute of your company than for all the promotion in the world.'

Thus he stayed and talked to her, and told her interesting details of his native place, and incidents of his childhood, till she was in a simmer of distress at his recklessness in remaining. It was only because she insisted on bidding him good-night and leaving the wall that he returned to his quarters.

The next time that she saw him he was without the stripes that had adorned his sleeve. He had been broken to the level of private for his lateness that night; and as Phyllis considered herself to be the cause of his disgrace her sorrow was great. But the position was now reversed; it was his turn to cheer her.

'Don't grieve, *meine Liebliche!*[10] he said. 'I have got a remedy for whatever comes. First, even supposing I regain my stripes, would your father allow you to marry a non-commissioned officer in the York Hussars?'

She flushed. This practical step had not been in her mind in relation to such an unrealistic person as he was; and a moment's reflection was enough for it. 'My father would not — certainly would not,' she answered unflinchingly. 'It cannot be thought of! My dear friend, please do forget me; I fear I am ruining you and your prospects!'

'Not at all!' said he. 'You are giving this country of yours just sufficient interest to me to make me care to keep alive in it. If my dear land were here also, and my old parent, with you, I could be happy as I am, and would do my best as a soldier. But it is not so. And now listen. This is my plan. That you go with me to my own country, and be my wife there, and live there, with my mother and me. I am not a Hanoverian, as you know, though I entered the army as such; my country is by the Saar, and is at peace with France, and if I were once in it I should be free.'

'But how get there?' she asked. Phyllis had been rather amazed than shocked at his proposition. Her position in her father's house was growing irksome and painful in the extreme; his parental affection seemed to be quite dried up. She was not a native of the village, like all the joyous girls around her; and in some way Matthäus Tina had infected her with his own passionate longing for his country, and mother, and home.

'But how?' she repeated, finding that he did not answer. 'Will you buy your discharge?'

'Ah, no,' he said. 'That's impossible in these times. No; I came here against my will; why should I not escape? Now is the time, as we shall soon be striking camp, and I might see you no more. This is my scheme. I will ask you to meet me on the highway two miles off, on some calm night next week that may be appointed. There will be nothing unbecoming in it, or to cause

---

[10] meine Liebliche — my love

you shame; you will not fly alone with me, for I will bring with me my devoted young friend Christoph, an Alsatian,[11] who has lately joined the regiment, and who has agreed to assist in this enterprise. We shall have come from yonder harbour, where we shall have examined the boats, and found one suited to our purpose. Christoph has already a chart of the Channel, and we will then go to the harbour, and at midnight cut the boat from her moorings, and row away round the point out of sight; and by the next morning we are on the coast of France, near Cherbourg. The rest is easy, for I have saved money for the land journey, and can get a change of clothes. I will write to my mother, who will meet us on the way.'

He added details in reply to her inquiries, which left no doubt in Phyllis's mind of the feasibility of the undertaking. But its magnitude almost appalled her; and it is questionable if she would ever have gone further in the wild adventure if, on entering the house that night, her father had not accosted her in the most significant terms.

'How about the York Hussars?' he said.

'They are still at the camp; but they are soon going away, I believe.'

'It is useless for you to attempt to cloak your actions in that way. You have been meeting one of those fellows; you have been seen walking with him – foreign barbarians, not much better than the French themselves! I have made up my mind – don't speak a word till I have done, please! – I have made up my mind that you shall stay here no longer while they are on the spot. You shall go to your aunt's.'

It was useless for her to protest that she had never taken a walk with any soldier or man under the sun except himself. Her protestations were feeble, too, for though he was not literally correct in his assertion, he was virtually only half in error.

The house of her father's sister was a prison to Phyllis. She had quite recently undergone experience of its gloom; and when her father went on to direct her to pack what would be necessary for her to take, her heart died within her. In after years she never attempted to excuse her conduct during this week of agitation; but the result of her self-communing was that she decided to join in the scheme of her lover and his friend, and fly to the country which he had coloured with such lovely hues in her imagination. She always said that the one feature in his proposal which overcame her hesitation was the obvious purity and straightforwardness of his intentions. He showed himself to be so virtuous and kind; he treated her with a respect to which she had never before been accustomed; and she was braced to the obvious risks of the voyage by her confidence in him.

---

[11] *an Alsatian* – from Alsace, a region on the border between Germany and France

IV

It was on a soft, dark evening of the following week that they engaged in the adventure. Tina was to meet her at a point in the highway at which the lane to the village branched off. Christoph was to go ahead of them to the harbour where the boat lay, row it round the Nothe[12] – or Look-out as it was called in those days – and pick them up on the other side of the promontory, which they were to reach by crossing the harbour-bridge on foot, and climbing over the Look-out hill.

As soon as her father had ascended to his room she left the house, and, bundle in hand, proceeded at a trot along the lane. At such an hour not a soul was afoot anywhere in the village, and she reached the junction of the lane with the highway unobserved. Here she took up her position in the obscurity formed by the angle of a fence, whence she could discern every one who approached along the turnpike-road,[13] without being herself seen.

She had not remained thus waiting for her lover longer than a minute – though from the tension of her nerves the lapse of even that short time was trying – when, instead of the expected footsteps, the stage-coach could be heard descending the hill. She knew that Tina would not show himself till the road was clear, and waited impatiently for the coach to pass. Nearing the corner where she was it slackened speed, and, instead of going by as usual, drew up within a few yards of her. A passenger alighted, and she heard his voice. It was Humphrey Gould's.

He had brought a friend with him, and luggage. The luggage was deposited on the grass, and the coach went on its route to the royal watering-place.

'I wonder where that young man is with the horse and trap?' said her former admirer to his companion. 'I hope we shan't have to wait here long. I told him half-past nine o'clock precisely.'

'Have you got her present safe?'

'Phyllis's? O, yes. It is in this trunk. I hope it will please her.'

'Of course it will. What woman would not be pleased with such a handsome peace-offering?'

'Well – she deserves it. I've treated her rather badly. But she has been in my mind these last two days much more than I should care to confess to everybody. Ah, well; I'll say no more about that. It cannot be that she is so bad as they make out. I am quite sure that a girl of her good wit would know better than to get entangled with any of those Hanoverian soldiers. I won't believe it of her, and there's an end on't.'

---

[12] *the Nothe* – a piece of land jutting out into the sea near Weymouth
[13] *turnpike-road* – toll road

More words in the same strain were casually dropped as the two men waited; words which revealed to her, as by a sudden illumination, the enormity of her conduct. The conversation was at length cut off by the arrival of the man with the vehicle. The luggage was placed in it, and they mounted, and were driven on in the direction from which she had just come.

Phyllis was so conscious-stricken that she was at first inclined to follow them; but a moment's reflection led her to feel that it would only be bare justice to Matthäus to wait till he arrived, and explain candidly that she had changed her mind – difficult as the struggle would be when she stood face to face with him. She bitterly reproached herself for having believed reports which represented Humphrey Gould as false to his engagement, when, from what she now heard from his own lips, she gathered that he had been living full of trust in her. But she knew well enough who had won her love. Without him her life seemed a dreary prospect, yet the more she looked at his proposal the more she feared to accept it – so wild as it was, so vague, so venturesome. She had promised Humphrey Gould, and it was only his assumed faithlessness which had led her to treat that promise as nought. His solicitude in bringing her these gifts touched her; her promise must be kept, and esteem must take the place of love. She would preserve her self-respect. She would stay at home, and marry him, and suffer.

Phyllis had thus braced herself to an exceptional fortitude when, a few minutes later, the outline of Matthäus Tina appeared behind a field-gate, over which he lightly leapt as she stepped forward. There was no evading it, he pressed her to his breast.

'It is the first and last time!' she wildly thought as she stood encircled by his arms.

How Phyllis got through the terrible ordeal of that night she could never clearly recollect. She always attributed her success in carrying out her resolve to her lover's honour, for as soon as she declared to him in feeble words that she had changed her mind, and felt that she could not, dared not, fly with him, he forbore to urge her, grieved as he was at her decision. Unscrupulous pressure on his part, seeing how romantically she had become attached to him, would no doubt have turned the balance in his favour. But he did nothing to tempt her unduly or unfairly.

On her side, fearing for his safety, she begged him to remain. This, he declared, could not be. 'I cannot break faith with my friend.' said he. Had he stood alone he would have abandoned his plan. But Christoph, with the boat and compass and chart, was waiting on the shore; the tide would soon turn; his mother had been warned of his coming; go he must.

Many precious minutes were lost while he tarried, unable to tear himself away, Phyllis held to her resolve, though it cost her many a bitter pang. At last they parted, and he went down the hill. Before his footsteps had quite died away she felt a desire to behold at least his outline once more, and running noiselessly after him regained view of his diminishing figure. For one moment she was sufficiently excited to be on the point of rushing forward and linking her fate with his. But she could not. The courage which at the critical instant failed Cleopatra of Egypt[14] could scarcely be expected of Phyllis Grove.

A dark shape, similar to his own, joined him in the highway. It was Christoph, his friend. She could see no more; they had hastened on in the direction of the town and harbour, four miles ahead. With a feeling akin to despair she turned and slowly pursued her way homeward.

Tattoo sounded in the camp; but there was no camp for her now. It was as dead as the camp of the Assyrians after the passage of the Destroying Angel.[15]

She noiselessly entered the house, seeing nobody, and went to bed. Grief, which kept her awake at first, ultimately wrapped her in a heavy sleep. The next morning her father met her at the foot of the stairs.

'Mr Gould is come!' he said triumphantly.

Humphrey was staying at the inn, and had already called to inquire for her. He had brought her a present of a very handsome looking-glass in a frame of *repoussé*[16] silverwork, which her father held in his hand. He had promised to call again in the course of an hour, to ask Phyllis to walk with him.

Pretty mirrors were rarer in country-houses at that day than they are now, and the one before her won Phyllis's admiration. She looked into it, saw how heavy her eyes were, and endeavoured to brighten them. She was in that wretched state of mind which leads a woman to move mechanically onward in what she conceives to be her allotted path. Mr Humphrey had, in his undemonstrative way, been adhering all along to the old understanding; it was for her to do the same, and to say not a word of her own lapse. She put on her bonnet and tippet,[17] and when he arrived at the hour named she was at the door awaiting him.

V

Phyllis thanked him for his beautiful gift; but the talking was soon entirely on Humphrey's side as they walked along. He told her of the latest movements

[14] *failed Cleopatra of Egypt* – in Shakespeare's play, *Anthony and Cleopatra*, Cleopatra runs away from Caesar in a sea battle

[15] *the Destroying Angel* – which brought a storm to Elijah in The Bible

[16] repoussé – a technique for beating silver

[17] *tippet* – a shawl

of the world of fashion – a subject which she willingly discussed to the exclusion of anything more personal – and his measured language helped to still her disquieted heart and brain. Had not her own sadness been what it was she must have observed his embarrassment. At last he abruptly changed the subject.

'I am glad you are pleased with my little present,' he said. 'The truth is that I brought it to propitiate 'ee, and to get you to help me out of a mighty difficulty.'

It was inconceivable to Phyllis that this independent bachelor – whom she admired in some respects – could have a difficulty.

'Phyllis – I'll tell you my secret at once; for I have a monstrous secret to confide before I can ask your counsel. The case is, then, that I am married: yes, I have privately married a dear young belle; and if you knew her, and I hope you will, you would say everything in her praise. But she is not quite the one that my father would have chose for me – you know the paternal idea as well as I – and I have kept it secret. There will be a terrible noise, no doubt; but I think that with your help I may get over it. If you would only do me this good turn – when I have told my father, I mean – say that you never could have married me, you know, or something of that sort – 'pon my life it will help to smooth the way vastly. I am so anxious to win him round to my point of view, and not to cause any estrangement.'

What Phyllis replied she scarcely knew, or how she counselled him as to his unexpected situation. Yet the relief that his announcement brought her was perceptible. To have confided her trouble in return was what her aching heart longed to do; and had Humphrey been a woman she would instantly have poured out her tale. But to him she feared to confess; and there was a real reason for silence, till a sufficient time had elapsed to allow her lover and his comrade to get out of harm's way.

As soon as she reached home again she sought a solitary place, and spent the time in half regretting that she had not gone away, and in dreaming over the meetings with Matthäus Tina from their beginning to their end. In his own country, amongst his own countrywomen, he would possibly soon forget her, even to her very name.

Her listlessness was such that she did not go out of the house for several days. There came a morning which broke in fog and mist, behind which the dawn could be discerned in greenish grey; and the outlines of the tents, and the rows of horses at the ropes. The smoke from the canteen fires drooped heavily.

The spot at the bottom of the garden where she had been accustomed to climb the wall to meet Matthäus, was the only inch of English ground in which she took any interest; and in spite of the disagreeable haze prevailing she walked out there till she reached the well-known corner. Every blade of grass was weighted with little liquid globes, and slugs and snails had crept out upon the plots. She could hear the usual faint noises from the camp, and in the other direction the trot of farmers on the road to the town, for it was market-day. She observed that her frequent visits to this corner had quite trodden down the grass in the angle of the wall, and left marks of garden soil on the stepping-stones by which she had mounted to look over the top. Seldom having gone there till dusk, she had not considered that her traces might be visible by day. Perhaps it was these which had revealed her trysts to her father.

While she paused in melancholy regard, she fancied that the customary sounds from the tents were changing their character. Indifferent as Phyllis was to camp doings now, she mounted by the steps to the old place. What she beheld at first awed and perplexed her; then she stood rigid, her fingers hooked to the wall, her eyes staring out of her head, and her face as if hardened to stone.

On the open green stretching before her all the regiments in the camp were drawn up in line, in the mid-front of which two empty coffins lay on the ground. The unwonted sounds which she had noticed came from an advancing procession. It consisted of the band of the York Hussars playing a dead march; next two soldiers of that regiment in a mourning coach, guarded on each side, and accompanied by two priests. Behind came a crowd of rustics who had been attracted by the event. The melancholy procession marched along the front of the line, returned to the centre, and halted beside the coffins, where the two condemned men were blind-folded, and each placed kneeling on his coffin; a few minutes' pause was now given, while they prayed.

A firing-party of twenty-four men stood ready with levelled carbines.[18] The commanding officer, who had his sword drawn, waved it through some cuts of the sword-exercise till he reached the downward stroke, whereat the firing party discharged their volley. The two victims fell, one upon his face across his coffin, the other backwards.

As the volley resounded there arose a shriek from the wall of Dr Grove's garden, and some one fell down inside; but nobody among the spectators without noticed it at the time. The two executed Hussars were Matthäus Tina and his friend Christoph. The soldiers on guard placed the bodies in the coffins almost instantly; but the colonel of the regiment, an Englishman, rode up and exclaimed in a stern voice: 'Turn them out – as an example to the men!'

The coffins were lifted endwise, and the dead Germans flung out upon their faces on the grass. Then all the regiments wheeled in sections, and

[18] *carbines* – short, light muskets

marched past the spot in slow time. When the survey was over the corpses were again coffined, and borne away.

Meanwhile Dr Grove, attracted by the noise of the volley, had rushed out into his garden, where he saw his wretched daughter lying motionless against the wall. She was taken indoors, but it was long before she recovered consciousness; and for weeks they despaired of her reason.

It transpired that the luckless deserters from the York Hussars had cut the boat from her moorings in the adjacent harbour, according to their plan, and, with two other comrades who were smarting under ill-treatment from their colonel, had sailed in safety across the Channel. But mistaking their bearings they steered into Jersey, thinking that island the French coast. Here they were perceived to be deserters, and delivered up to the authorities. Matthäus and Christoph interceded for the other two at the court-martial, saying that it was entirely by the former's representations that these were induced to go. Their sentence was accordingly commuted to flogging, the death punishment being reserved for their leaders.

The visitor to the well-known old Georgian watering-place, who may care to ramble to the neighbouring village under the hills, and examine the register of burials, will there find two entries in these words:

Matth: Tina (Corpl.) in His Majesty's Regmt. of York Hussars, and Shot for Desertion, was Buried June 30th, 1801, aged 22 years. Born in the town of Sarrbruk, Germany.

Christoph Bless, belonging to His Majesty's Regmt. of York Hussars, who was Shot for Desertion, was Buried June 30th, 1801, aged 22 years. Born at Lothaargen, Alsatia.

Their graves were dug at the back of the little church, near the wall. There is no memorial to mark the spot, but Phyllis pointed it out to me. While she lived she used to keep their mounds neat; but now they are overgrown with nettles, and sunk nearly flat. The older villagers, however, who know of the episode from their parents, still recollect the place where the soldiers lie. Phyllis lies near.

Désirée's Baby

Kate Chopin

As the day was pleasant, Madame Valmondé drove over to L'Abri to see Désirée and the baby.

It made her laugh to think of Désirée with a baby. Why, it seemed but yesterday that Désirée was little more than a baby herself; when Monsieur in riding through the gateway of Valmondé had found her lying asleep in the shadow of the big stone pillar.

The little one awoke in his arms and began to cry for 'Dada.' That was as much as she could do or say. Some people thought she might have strayed there of her own accord, for she was of the toddling age. The prevailing belief was that she had been purposely left by a party of Texans, whose canvas-covered wagon, late in the day, had crossed the ferry that Coton Maïs kept, just below the plantation. In time Madame Valmondé abandoned every speculation but the one that Désirée had been sent to her by a beneficent Providence[1] to be the child of her affection, seeing that she was without child of the flesh. For the girl grew to be beautiful and gentle, affectionate and sincere – the idol of Valmondé.

It was no wonder, when she stood one day against the stone pillar in whose shadow she had lain asleep, eighteen years before, that Armand Aubigny riding by and seeing her there, had fallen in love with her. That was the way all the Aubignys fell in love, as if struck by a pistol shot. The wonder was that he had not loved her before; for he had known her since his father brought him home from Paris, a boy of eight, after his mother died there. The passion that awoke in him that day, when he saw her at the gate, swept along like an avalanche, or like a prairie fire, or like anything that drives headlong over all obstacles.

Monsieur Valmondé grew practical and wanted things well considered: that is, the girl's obscure origin. Armand looked into her eyes and did not care. He was reminded that she was nameless. What did it matter about a name when he could give her one of the oldest and proudest in Louisiana? He ordered the *corbeille*[2] from Paris, and contained himself with what patience he could until it arrived; then they were married.

Madame Valmondé had not seen Désirée and the baby for four weeks. When she reached L'Abri she shuddered at the first sight of it, as she always did. It was a sad looking place, which for many years had not known the

---

[1] *Providence* – fate

[2] *corbeille* – a present of wedding clothes

gentle presence of a mistress, old Monsieur Aubigny having married and buried his wife in France, and she having loved her own land too well ever to leave it. The roof came down steep and black like a cowl, reaching out beyond the wide galleries that encircled the yellow stuccoed house. Big, solemn oaks grew close to it, and their thick-leaved, far-reaching branches shadowed it like a pall. Young Aubigny's rule was a strict one, too, and under it his negroes had forgotten how to be gay, as they had been during the old master's easy-going and indulgent lifetime.

The young mother was recovering slowly, and lay full length, in her soft white muslins and laces, upon a couch. The baby was beside her, upon her arm, where he had fallen asleep, at her breast. The yellow nurse woman sat beside a window fanning herself.

Madame Valmondé bent her portly figure over Désirée and kissed her, holding her an instant tenderly in her arms. Then she turned to the child.

'This is not the baby!' she exclaimed, in startled tones. French was the language spoken at Valmondé in those days.

'I knew you would be astonished,' laughed Désirée, 'at the way he has grown. The little *cocbon de lait!*[3] Look at his legs, mamma, and his hands and fingernails, – real finger-nails. Zandrine had to cut them this morning. Is n't it true, Zandrine?'

The woman bowed her turbaned head majestically, 'Mais si, Madame.'

'And the way he cries,' went on Désirée, 'is deafening. Armand heard him the other day as far away as La Blanche's cabin.'

Madame Valmondé had never removed her eyes from the child. She lifted it and walked with it over to the window that was lightest. She scanned the baby narrowly, then looked as searchingly at Zandrine, whose face was turned to gaze across the fields.

'Yes, the child has grown, has changed,' said Madame Valmondé, slowly, as she replaced it beside its mother. 'What does Armand say?'

Désirées face became suffused with a glow that was happiness itself.

'Oh, Armand is the proudest father in the parish, I believe, chiefly because it is a boy, to bear his name; though he says not – that he would have loved a girl as well. But I know it is n't true. I know he says that to please me. And mamma,' she added, drawing Madame Valmondé's head down to her and speaking in a whisper, 'he has n't punished one of them – not one of them – since baby is born. Even Négrillon, who pretended to have burnt his leg that he might rest from work – he only laughed, and said Négrillon was a great scamp. Oh, mamma, I'm so happy; it frightens me.'

---

[3] cocbon de lait – this affectionate name for a baby was originally *cochon de lait* meaning 'little sucking pig'.

What Désirée said was true. Marriage, and later the birth of his son had softened Armand Aubigny's imperious and exacting nature greatly. This was what made the gentle Désirée so happy, for she loved him desperately. When he frowned she trembled, but loved him. When he smiled, she asked no greater blessing of God. But Armand's dark, handsome face had not often been disfigured by frowns since the day he fell in love with her.

When the baby was about three months old, Désirée awoke one day to the conviction that there was something in the air menacing her peace. It was at first too subtle to grasp. It had only been a disquieting suggestion; an air of mystery among the blacks; unexpected visits from far-off neighbours who could hardly account for their coming. Then a strange, an awful change in her husband's manner, which she dared not ask him to explain. When he spoke to her, it was with averted eyes, from which the old love-light seemed to have gone out. He absented himself from home; and when there, avoided her presence and that of her child, without excuse. And the very spirit of Satan seemed suddenly to take hold of him in his dealings with the slaves. Désirée was miserable enough to die.

She sat in her room, one hot afternoon, in her *peignoir*,[4] listlessly drawing through her fingers the strands of her long, silky brown hair that hung about her shoulders. The baby, half naked, lay asleep upon her own great mahogany bed, that was like a sumptuous throne, with its satin-lined half-canopy. One of La Blanche's little quadroon[5] boys half naked too – stood fanning the child slowly with a fan of peacock feathers. Désirées eyes had been fixed absently and sadly upon the baby, while she was striving to penetrate the threatening mist that she felt closing about her. She looked from her child to the boy who stood beside him, and back again, over and over. 'Ah!' It was a cry that she could not help; which she was not conscious of having uttered. The blood turned like ice in her veins, and a clammy moisture gathered upon her face.

She tried to speak to the little quadroon boy; but no sound would come, at first. When he heard his name uttered, he looked up, and his mistress was pointing to the door. He laid aside the great, soft fan, and obediently stole away, over the polished floor, on his bare tiptoes.

She stayed motionless, with gaze riveted upon her child, and her face the picture of fright.

Presently her husband entered the room, and without noticing her, went to a table and began to search among some papers which covered it.

'Armand,' she called to him, in a voice which must have stabbed him, if he was human. But he did not notice. 'Armand,' she said again. Then she rose

4   peignoir – a bathrobe or dressing gown
5   *quadroon* – a person of mixed race but with one white parent

35

and tottered towards him. 'Armand,' she panted once more, clutching his arm, 'look at our child. What does it mean? tell me.'

He coldly but gently loosened her fingers from about his arm and thrust the hand away from him. 'Tell me what it means!' she cried despairingly.

'It means,' he answered lightly, 'that the child is not white; it means that you are not white.'

A quick conception of all that this accusation meant for her nerved her with unwonted courage to deny it. 'It is a lie; it is not true, I am white! Look at my hair, it is brown; and my eyes are gray, Armand, you know they are gray. And my skin is fair,' seizing his wrist. 'Look at my hand; whiter than yours, Armand,' she laughed hysterically.

'As white as La Blanche's,' he returned cruelly; and went away leaving her alone with their child.

When she could hold a pen in her hand, she sent a despairing letter to Madame Valmondé.

'My mother, they tell me I am not white. Armand has told me I am not white. For God's sake tell them it is not true. You must know it is not true. I shall die. I must die. I cannot be so unhappy, and live.'

The answer that came was as brief:

'My own Désirée: Come home to Valmondé; back to your mother who loves you. Come with your child.'

When the letter reached Désirée she went with it to her husband's study, and laid it open upon the desk before which he sat. She was like a stone image; silent, white, motionless after she placed it there.

In silence he ran his cold eyes over the written words. He said nothing. 'Shall I go, Armand?' she asked in tones sharp with agonized suspense.

'Yes, go.'

'Do you want me to go?'

'Yes, I want you to go.'

He thought Almighty God had dealt cruelly and unjustly with him; and felt, somehow, that he was paying Him back in kind when he stabbed thus into his wife's soul. Moreover he no longer loved her, because of the unconscious injury she had brought upon his home and his name.

She turned away like one stunned by a blow, and walked slowly towards the door, hoping he would call her back.

'Good-by, Armand,' she moaned.

He did not answer her. That was his last blow at fate.

Désirée went in search of her child. Zandrine was pacing the sombre gallery with it. She took the little one from the nurse's arms with no word of explanation, and descending the steps, walked away, under the live-oak branches.

It was an October afternoon; the sun was just sinking. Out in the still fields the negroes were picking cotton.

Désirée had not changed the thin white garment nor the slippers which she wore. Her hair was uncovered and the sun's rays brought a golden gleam from its brown meshes. She did not take the broad, beaten road which led to the far-off plantation of Valmondé. She walked across a deserted field, where the stubble bruised her tender feet, so delicately shod, and tore her thin gown to shreds.

She disappeared among the reeds and willows that grew thick along the banks of the deep, sluggish bayou;[6] and she did not come back again.

Some weeks later there was a curious scene enacted at L'Abri. In the centre of the smoothly swept back yard was a great bonfire. Armand Aubigny sat in the wide hallway that commanded a view of the spectacle; and it was he who dealt out to a half dozen negroes the material which kept this fire ablaze.

A graceful cradle of willow, with all its dainty furbishings, was laid upon the pyre, which had already been fed with the richness of a priceless *layette*.[7] Then there were silk gowns, and velvet and satin ones added to these; laces, too, and embroideries; bonnets and gloves; for the *corbeille* had been of rare quality.

The last thing to go was a tiny bundle of letters; innocent little scribblings that Désirée had sent to him during the days of their espousal. There was the remnant of one back in the drawer from which he took them. But it was not Désirée's; it was part of an old letter from his mother to his father. He read it. She was thanking God for the blessing of her husband's love: —

'But, above all,' she wrote, 'night and day, I thank the good God for having so arranged our lives that our dear Armand will never know that his mother, who adores him, belongs to the race that is cursed with the brand of slavery.'

---

[6] *bayou* – a marshy area made by the overflow from lakes and rivers. A typical feature of the Louisiana area where this story is set.
[7] layette – a set of clothing for a new-born child

Letters

To Cassandra (May 1801)

Jane Austen

Paragon: Tuesday May 5 1801

My dear Cassandra

I have the pleasure of writing from my *own* room up two pairs of stairs, with everything very comfortable about me.

Our journey here was perfectly free from accident or event; we changed horses at the end of every stage, and paid at almost every turnpike.[1] We had charming weather, hardly any dust, and were exceedingly agreeable, as we did not speak above once in three miles.

Between Luggershall and Everley we made our grand meal, and then with admiring astonishment perceived in what a magnificent manner our support had been provided for. We could not with the utmost exertion consume above the twentieth part of the beef. The cucumber will, I believe, be a very acceptable present, as my uncle talks of having inquired the price of one lately, when he was told a shilling.

We had a very neat chaise[2] from Devizes; it looked almost as well as a gentleman's, at least as a very shabby gentleman's; in spite of this advantage, however, we were above three hours coming from thence to Paragon, and it was half after seven by your clocks before we entered the house.

Frank, whose black head was in waiting in the Hall window, received us very kindly; and his master and mistress did not show less cordiality. They both look very well, though my aunt has a violent cough. We drank tea as soon as we arrived, and so ends the account of our journey, which my mother bore without any fatigue.

How do you do to-day? I hope you improve in sleeping – I think you must, because *I* fall off; I have been awake ever since five and sooner; I fancy I had too much clothes over me; I thought I *should* by the feel of them before I went to bed, but I had not courage to alter them. I am warmer here without any fire than I have been lately with an excellent one.

Well, and so the good news is confirmed, and Martha triumphs. My uncle and aunt seemed quite surprised that you and my father were not coming sooner.

I have given the soap and the basket, and each have been kindly

[1] *turnpike* – a toll gate
[2] *chaise* – a type of carriage

received. *One* thing only among all our concerns has not arrived in safety: when I got into the chaise at Devizes I discovered that your drawing ruler was broke in two; it is just at the top where the crosspiece is fastened on. I beg pardon.

There is to be only one more ball – next Monday is the day. The Chamberlaynes are still here. I begin to think better of Mrs C —— , and upon recollection believe she has rather a long chin than otherwise, as she remembers us in Gloucestershire when we were very charming young women.

The first view of Bath in fine weather does not answer my expectations; I think I see more distinctly through rain. The sun was got behind everything, and the appearance of the place from the top of Kingsdown was all vapour, shadow, smoke, and confusion.

I fancy we are to have a house in Seymour Street, or thereabouts. My uncle and aunt both like the situation. I was glad to hear the former talk of all the houses in New King Street as too small; it was my own idea of them. I had not been two minutes in the dining-room before he questioned me with all his accustomary eager interest about Frank and Charles, their views and intentions. I did my best to give information.

I am not without hopes of tempting Mrs Lloyd to settle in Bath; meat is only 8*d*. per pound, butter 12*d*., and cheese 9½*d*. You must carefully conceal from her, however, the exorbitant price of fish: a salmon has been sold at 2*s*. 9*d*. per pound the whole fish. The Duchess of York's removal is expected to make that article more reasonable – and till it really appears so, say nothing about salmon.

Tuesday night. When my uncle went to take his second glass of water I walked with him, and in our morning's circuit we looked at two houses in Green Park Buildings, one of which pleased me very well. We walked all over it except into the garret; the dining-room is of a comfortable size, just as large as you like to fancy it; the second room about 14 ft. square. The apartment over the drawing-room pleased me particularly, because it is divided into two, the smaller one a very nice-sized dressing-room, which upon occasion might admit a bed. The aspect is south-east. The only doubt is about the dampness of the offices, of which there were symptoms.

Wednesday. Mrs Mussell has got my gown, and I will endeavour to explain what her intentions are. It is to be a round gown, with a jacket and a frock front, like Cath. Bigg's, to open at the side. The jacket is all in one with the body, and comes as far as the pocket-holes – about half a quarter of a yard deep, I suppose, all the way round, cut off straight at the corners with a broad hem. No fulness appears either in the body or the flap; the back is quite plain in this form ⫿, and the sides equally so. The front is sloped round to the bosom and drawn in, and there is to be a frill of the same to put on occasionally when all ones handkerchiefs are dirty – which frill *must* fall back. She is to put two breadths and a-half in the tail, and no gores – gores not being so much worn as they were. There is nothing new in the sleeves: they are to be plain, with a fulness of the same falling down and gathered up underneath, just like some of Martha's, or perhaps a little longer. Low in the back behind, and a belt of the same. I can think of nothing more, though I am afraid of not being particular enough.

My mother has ordered a new bonnet, and so have I; both white strip, trimmed with white ribbon. I find my straw bonnet looking very much like other people's, and quite as smart. Bonnets of cambric muslin[3] on the plan of Lady Bridges' are a good deal worn, and some of them are very pretty; but I shall defer one of that sort till your arrival. Bath is getting so very empty that I am not afraid of doing too little. Black gauze cloaks are worn as much as anything. I shall write again in a day or two. Best love.

Yours ever, J.A.

We have had Mrs. Lillingstone and the Chamberlaynes to call on us. My mother was very much struck with the odd looks of the two latter; *I* have only seen *her*. Mrs. Busby drinks tea and plays at cribbage here to-morrow; and on Friday, I believe, we go to the Chamberlaynes'. Last night we walked by the Canal.

[3] *cambric muslin* – a fine white linen from Cambrai in northern France

To his father
(October or November 1805)

Sam

Honoured Fathre,

This comes to tell you that I am alive and hearty except three fingers; but that's not much, it might have been my head. I told brother Tom I should like to see a greadly battle, and I have seen one, and we have peppered the Combined[1] rarely (off Trafalgar); and for the matter of that, they fought us pretty tightish for French and Spanish. Three of our mess[2] are killed, and four more of us winged. But to tell you the truth of it, when the game began, I wished myself at Warnborough with my plough again; but when they had given us one duster, and I found myself snug and tight, I set to in good earnest, and thought no more about being killed than if I were at Murrell Green Fair, and I was presently as busy and as black as a collier. How my fingers got knocked overboard I don't know, but off they are, and I never missed them till I wanted them. You see, by my writing, it was my left hand, so I can write to you and fight for my King yet. We have taken a rare parcel of ships, but the wind is so rough we cannot bring them home, else I should roll in money, so we are busy smashing 'em, and blowing 'em up wholesale.

Our dear Admiral Nelson is killed! so we have paid pretty sharply for licking 'em. I never set eyes on him, for which I am both sorry and glad; for to be sure, I should like to have seen him – but then, all the men in our ship are such soft toads, they have done nothing but blast their eyes, and cry, ever since he was killed. God bless you! chaps that fought like the devil, sit down and cry like a wench. I am still in the *Royal Sovereign*, but the Admiral has left her, for she is like a horse without a bridle, so he is in a frigate that he may be here and there and everywhere, for he's as *cute* as here and there one, and as bold as a lion, for all he can cry! I saw his tears with my own eyes, when the boat hailed and said my Lord was dead. So no more at present from

Your dutiful Son,
Sam

---

[1] *the Combined* – the combined French and Spanish fleets against whom Nelson and the British Navy fought at the Battle of Trafalgar.

[2] *our mess* – the sailors' eating and living area on board a ship

To Thomas Hitchener (14 May 1812)

Percy Bysshe Shelley

Nantgwillt, May 14. 1812

Sir

If you have always considered *character* a posession of the first consequence you & I essentially differ. If you think that an admission of your inferiority to the world leaves any corner by which yourself & character may aspire beyond it's reach, we differ there again. In short, to be candid, I am deceived in my conception of your character. –

I had some difficulty in stifling an indignant surprise on reading the sentence of your letter in which *you* refuse my invitation to your daughter. How are you entitled to do this? who made you her governor? did you receive this refusal from her to communicate to me? No you have not. – How are *you* then constituted to answer a question which can only be addressed to *her*? believe me such an assumption is as impotent as it is immoral, you may cause your daughter much anxiety many troubles, you may stretch her on a bed of sickness, you may destroy her body, but are defied to shake her mind. – She is now very ill. *You* have agitated her mind until her frame is seriously deranged – take care Sir, you may destroy her by disease, but her mind is free, *that* you cannot hurt. – Your ideas of *Propriety* (or to express myself clearer, of *morals*) are all founded on considerations of *profit*. I do not mean money but *profit* in its extended sense; – As to your daughters welfare on that *she* is competent to judge or at least she alone has a right to decide. With respect to your own comfort you of course do right to consult it, that she has done so you ought to be more grateful than you appear. – But how can you demand as a right what has been generously conceded as a favor; you do right to consult your own comfort, but the whole world besides may surely be excused.

Neither the laws of Nature, nor of England have made children private property –

Adieu, when next I hear from you, I hope that time will have liberalized your sentiments.

Your's truly
P. B. Shelley

To Daniel Maclise (12 March 1841)

Charles Dickens

Devonshire Terrace.
Friday Evening
March The Twelfth 1841.

Mr Dear Maclise,

You will be greatly shocked and grieved to hear that the Raven is no more. He expired to-day at a few minutes after Twelve o'Clock at noon. He had been ailing (as I told you t'other night) for a few days, but we anticipated no serious result, conjecturing that a portion of the white paint he swallowed last summer might be lingering about his vitals without having any serious effect upon his constitution. Yesterday afternoon he was taken so much worse that I sent an express for the medical gentleman (Mr Herring) who promptly attended, and administered a powerful dose of castor oil. Under the influence of this medicine, he recovered so far as to be able at 8 o'Clock p.m. to bite Topping. His night was peaceful. This morning at daybreak he appeared better; received (agreeably to the doctor's directions) another dose of castor oil; and partook plentifully of some warm gruel, the flavour of which he appeared to relish. Towards eleven o'Clock he was so much worse that it was found necessary to muffle the stable knocker. At half past, or thereabouts, he was heard talking to himself about the horse and Topping's family, and to add some incoherent expressions which are supposed to have been either a foreboding of his approaching dissolution, or some wishes relative to the disposal of his little property consisting chiefly of halfpence which he had buried in different parts of the garden. On the clock striking twelve he appeared slightly agitated, but he soon recovered, walked twice or thrice along the coach-house, stopped to bark, staggered, exclaimed 'Halloa old girl!' (his favourite expression) and died.

He behaved throughout with a decent fortitude, equanimity, and self-possession, which cannot be too much admired. I deeply regret that being in ignorance of his danger I did not attend to receive his last instructions. Something remarkable about his eyes occasioned Topping to run for the doctor at Twelve. When they returned together our friend was gone. It was the medical gentleman who informed me of his decease. He did it with great caution and delicacy, preparing me by the remark that 'a jolly queer start had taken place', but the shock was very great notwithstanding.

I am not wholly free from suspicions of poison – a malicious butcher has been heard to say that he would 'do' for him – this plea was, that he would not be molested in taking orders down the Mews, by any bird that wore a tail

– other persons have also been heard to threaten – among others, Charles Knight who has just started a weekly publication, price fourpence; Barnaby being, as you know, Threepence. I have directed a post mortem examination, and the body has been removed to Mr. Herring's school of Anatomy for that purpose.

I could wish, if you can take the trouble, that you would inclose this to Foster when you have read it. I cannot discharge the painful task of communication more than once. Were they Ravens who took Manna to somebody in the wilderness? At times I hope they were, and at others I fear they were not, or they would certainly have stolen it by the way. In profound sorrow, I am ever Your bereaved friend. CD.

Kate is as well as can be expected, but terribly low as you may suppose. The children seem rather glad of it. He bit their ancles. But that was play –

To the President of the United States (1854)

Chief Seattle

How can you buy or sell the sky, the warmth of the land? The idea is strange to us.

If we do not own the freshness of the air and the sparkle of the water, how can you buy them?

Every part of this earth is sacred to my people.

Every shining pine needle, every sandy shore, every mist in the dark woods, every clearing and humming insect is holy in the memory and experience of my people. The sap which courses through the trees carried the memories of the red man.

The white man's dead forget the country of their birth when they go to walk among the stars. Our dead never forget this beautiful earth, for it is the mother of the red man.

We are part of the earth and it is part of us. The perfumed flowers are our sisters; the deer, the horse, the great eagle, these are our brothers.

The rocky crests, the juices in the meadows, the body heat of the pony, and man – all belong to the same family.

So, when the Great Chief in Washington sends word that he wishes to buy our land, he asks much of us. The Great Chief sends word he will reserve us a place so that we can live comfortably to ourselves.

He will be our father and we will be his children. So we will consider your offer to buy our land.

But it will not be easy. For this land is sacred to us.

This shining water that moves in the streams and rivers is not just water but the blood of our ancestors.

If we sell you land, you must remember that it is sacred, and you must teach your children that it is sacred and that each ghostly reflection in the clear water of the lakes tells of events and memories in the life of my people.

The water's murmur is the voice of my father's father.

The rivers are our brothers, they quench our thirst. The rivers carry our canoes, and feed our children. If we sell you our land, you must remember, and teach your children, that the rivers are our brothers and yours, and you must henceforth give the rivers the kindness you would give any brother.

We know that the white man does not understand our ways. One portion of land is the same to him as the next, for he is a stranger who comes in the night and takes from the land whatever he needs.

The earth is not his brother, but his enemy, and when he has conquered it, he moves on.

He leaves his father's graves behind, and he does not care. He kidnaps the earth from his children, and he does not care.

His father's grave and his children's birthright, are forgotten. He treats his mother, the earth, and his brother, the sky, as things to be bought, plundered, sold like sheep or bright beads.

His appetite will devour the earth and leave behind only a desert.

I do not know. Our ways are different from your ways.

The sight of your cities pains the eyes of the red man. But perhaps it is because the red man is a savage and does not understand.

There is no quiet place in the white man's cities. No place to hear the unfurling of leaves in spring, or the rustle of an insect's wings.

But perhaps it is because I am a savage and do not understand.

The clatter only seems to insult the ears. And what is there to life if a man cannot hear the lonely cry of the whippoorwill[1] or the arguments of the frogs around a pond at night? I am a red man and do not understand.

The Indian prefers the soft sound of the wind darting over the face of a pond, and the smell of the wind itself, cleaned by a midday rain, or scented with the pinon pine.[2]

The air is precious to the red man, for all things share the same breath – the beast, the tree, the man, they all share the same breath.

The white man does not seem to notice the air he breathes. Like a man dying for many days, he is numb to the stench.

But if we sell you our land, you must remember that the air is precious to us, that the air shares its spirit with all the life it supports. The wind that gave our grandfather his first breath also receives his last sigh.

And if we sell you our land, you must keep it apart and sacred, as a place where even the white man can go to taste the wind that is sweetened by the meadow's flowers.

So we will consider your offer to buy our land. If we decide to accept, I will make one condition: the white man must treat the beasts of this land as his brother.

I am a savage and I do not understand any other way.

I have seen a thousand rotting buffaloes on the prairie, left by the white man who shot them from a passing train.

I am a savage and I do not understand how the smoking iron horse can be more important than the buffalo that we kill only to stay alive.

[1] *whippoorwill* – a large bird found throughout North America
[2] *pinon pine* – a type of pine tree usually found in the southern states of America

What is man without the beasts? If all the beasts were gone, man would die from a great loneliness of spirit.

For whatever happens to the beasts, soon happens to man. All things are connected.

You must teach your children that the ground beneath their feet is the ashes of your grandfathers. So that they will respect the land, tell your children that the earth is rich with the lives of our kin.

Teach your children what we have taught our children, that the earth is our mother.

Whatever befalls the earth befalls the sons of the earth. If men spit upon the ground, they spit upon themselves.

This we know: the earth does not belong to man; man belongs to the earth. This we know.

All things are connected like the blood which unites one family. All things are connected.

Whatever befalls the earth befalls the sons of the earth. Man did not weave the web of life: he is merely a strand in it. Whatever he does to the web, he does to himself.

Even the white man, whose God walks and talks with him as friend to friend, cannot be exempt from the common destiny.

We may be brothers after all.

We shall see.

One thing we know, which the white man may one day discover – our God is the same God.

You may think now that you own Him as you wish to own our land; but you cannot. He is the God of man, and His compassion is equal for the red man and the white.

This earth is precious to Him, and to harm the earth is to heap contempt on its Creator.

The whites too shall pass; perhaps sooner than all other tribes. Contaminate your bed, and you will one night suffocate in your own waste.

But in your perishing you will shine brightly, fired by the strength of the God who brought you to this land and for some special purpose gave you dominion over this land and over the red man.

That destiny is a mystery to us, for we do not understand when the buffalo are all slaughtered, the wild horses are tamed, the secret corners of the forest heavy with scent of many men, and the view of the ripe hills blotted by talking wires.

Where is the thicket? Gone.

Where is the eagle? Gone.

The end of living and the beginning of survival.

Poetry

Time

'Like as the waves make towards the pibled shore'

William Shakespeare

Like as the waves make towards the pibled[1] shore,
So do our minutes hasten to their end,
Each changing place with that which goes before,
In sequent toile all forwards do contend.
Nativity once in the maine[2] of light
Crawles to maturity, wherewith being crown'd,
Crooked eclipses gainst his gift confound[3].
And time that gave, doth now his gift confound.
Time doth transfixe the Horish[4] set on youth,
And delves the paralels in beauties brow,
Feedes on the rarities of natures truth,
And nothing stands but for his sieth[5] to mow.
   And yet to times in hope, my verse shall stand
   Praising thy worth, dispight[6] his cruell hand.

[1] *pibled* – pebbled
[2] *maine* – main part
[3] *confound* – take away
[4] *Horish* – old
[5] *sieth* – scythe
[6] *dispight* – despite

To Dianeme

Robert Herrick

Sweet, be not proud of those two eyes
Which starlike sparkle in their skies;
Nor be you proud that you can see
All hearts your captives, yours yet free;
Be you not proud of that rich hair
Which wantons with the love-sick air;
Whenas that ruby which you wear,
Sunk from the tip of your soft ear,
Will last to be a precious stone
When all your world of beauty's gone.

Ozymandias

Percy Bysshe Shelley

I met a traveller from an antique land
Who said: Two vast and trunkless legs of stone
Stand in the desert . . . Near them, on the sand,
Half sunk, a shattered visage[1] lies, whose frown,
And wrinkled lip, and sneer of cold command,
Tell that its sculptor well those passions read
Which yet survive, stamped on these lifeless things.
The hand that mocked them, and the heart that fed:
And on the pedestal these words appear:
'My name is Ozymandias, king of kings:
Look on my works, ye Mighty, and despair!'
Nothing beside remains. Round the decay
Of that colossal wreck, boundless and bare
The lone and level sands stretch far away.

[1] *visage* – face. All that remains of the statue are the legs and head.

On Wenlock Edge

A. E. Housman

On Wenlock Edge[1] the wood's in trouble;
His forest fleece the Wrekin[2] heaves;
The gale it plies the saplings double,
And thick on Severn snow the leaves.

'Twould blow like this through holt[3] and hanger[4]
When Uricon[5] the city stood:
'Tis the old wind in the old anger,
But then it threshed another wood.

Then, 'twas before my time, the Roman
At yonder heaving hill would stare:
The blood that warms an English yeoman,[6]
The thoughts that hurt him, they were there.

Then, like the wind through woods in riot,
Through him the gale of life blew high;
The tree of man was never quiet:
Then 'twas the Roman, now 'tis I.

The gale, it plies the saplings double,
It blows so hard, 'twill soon be gone:
Today the Roman and his trouble
Are ashes under Uricon.

[1] *Wenlock Edge* – a ridge of hills in Shropshire
[2] *Wrekin* – the name of a hill near Wenlock Edge and overlooking the Roman town of Viroconium (modern-day Wroxeter)
[3] *holt* – an otter's den
[4] *hanger* – a wood on a hillside
[5] *Uricon* – or Viroconium, the Roman town now Wroxeter in Shropshire
[6] *yeoman* – an English foot-soldier

Love

To Celia

Ben Jonson

Come my Celia, let us prove,
While we may, the sports of love;
Time will not be ours, for ever:
He, at length, our good will sever.
Spend not then his guifts[1] in vaine.
Sunnes, that set, may rise againe:
But if once we loose this light,
'Tis, with us, perpetuall night.
Why should we deferre[2] our joyes?
Fame, and rumor are but toyes.
Cannot we delude the eyes
Of a few poor houshold spyes?
Or his easier ears beguile,[3]
So removed by our wile?[4]
'Tis no sinne, loves fruit to steale,
But the sweet theft to reveale:
To be taken, to be seene,
These have crimes accounted beene.

[1] *guifts* – gifts
[2] *deferre* – delay
[3] *beguile* – trick
[4] *wile* – secrecy

The Spring

Thomas Carew

Now that the winter's gone, the earth hath lost
Her snow-white robes, and now no more the frost
Candies the grasse, or castes an ycie,[1] creame
Upon the silver Lake, or Chrystall streame;
But the warme Sunne thawes the benummed,[2] Earth,
And makes it tender, gives a sacred birth
To the dead Swallow; wakes in hollow tree
The drowzie Cuckow, and the Humble-Bee.
Now doe a quire[3] of chirping Minstrels bring
In tryumph to the world, the youthfull Spring.
The Vallies, hills and woods, in rich araye,[4]
Welcome the comming of the long'd for May.
Now all things smile; only my Love doth lowre:[5]
Nor hath the scalding Noon-day-Sunne the power,
To melt that marble yee,[6] which still doth hold
Her heart congeald, and makes her pittie cold.
The Oxe which lately did for shelter fly
Into the stall, doth now securely lie
In open fields; and love no more is made
By the fire side; but in the cooler shade
Amyutas[7] now doth with his Cloris[7] sleepe
Under a Sycamoure, and all things keepe
Time with the season, only shee doth carry
June in her eyes, in her heart *January*.

[1] *ycie*   icy
[2] *benummed* – numb or frozen
[3] *quire* – choir
[4] *araye* – decoration
[5] *lowre* – frown
[6] *yee* – eye
[7] Amyutas and Cloris – lovers from Classical mythology

The Bracelet: To Julia

Robert Herrick

Why I tie about thy wrist
Julia, this silken twist;
For what other reason is't
But to show there how, in part,
Thou my pretty captive art?
But thy bond-slave is my heart:
'Tis but silk that bindeth thee,
Knap[1] the thread and thou art free;
But, 'tis otherwise with me:
I am bound and fast bound, so
That from thee I cannot go;
If I could, I would not so.

[1] *Knap* – untie

'Youth gone and beauty gone if ever there'

Christina Rossetti

Youth gone and beauty gone if ever there
Dwelt beauty in so poor a face as this;
Youth gone and beauty, what remains of bliss?
I will not bind fresh roses in my hair,
To shame a cheek at best but little fair,
Leave youth his roses, who can bear a thorn –
I will not seek for blossoms anywhere,
Except such common flowers as blow with corn.
Youth gone and beauty gone, what doth remain?
The longing of a heart pent up forlorn,
A silent heart whose silence loves and longs;
The silence of a heart which sang its songs
While youth and beauty made a summer morn,
Silence of love that cannot sing again.

Sea Wrack[1]

Moira O'Neill

The wrack was dark an' shiny where it floated in the sea,
There was no one in the brown boat but only him an' me;
Him to cut the sea wrack, me to mind the boat,
An' not a word between us the hours we were afloat.
The wet wrack,
The sea wrack,
The wrack was strong to cut.

We laid it on the grey rocks to wither in the sun,
An' what should call my lad then, to sail from Cushendun?[2]
With a low moon, a full tide, a swell upon the deep
Him to sail the old boat, me to fall asleep.
The dry wrack,
The sea wrack,
The wrack was dead so soon.

There's fire low upon the rocks to burn the wrack to kelp,[3]
There's a boat gone down upon the Moyle,[4] an' sorra[5] one to help!
Him beneath the salt sea, me upon the shore;
By sunlight or moonlight we'll lift the wrack no more.
The dark wrack,
The sea wrack,
The wrack may drift ashore.

[1] *sea wrack* – a type of sea weed
[2] *Cushendun* – a town in Northern Ireland
[3] *kelp* – the ashes of sea weed from which iodine was obtained
[4] *Moyle* – an area of coastal water
[5] *sorra* – no one

Protest

A Ballad

Charles Lamb

In a costly palace Youth goes clad in gold
In a wretched workhouse[1] Age's limbs are cold:
There they sit, the old men by a shivering fire,
Still close and closer cowering, warmth is their desire.

In a costly palace, when the brave gallants dine,
They have store of venison[2] with old canary wine,
With singing and music, to heighten the cheer,
Coarse bits, with grudging are the pauper's best fare.

In costly palace Youth is still caressed
By a train of attendants, which laugh at my young Lord's jest;
In a wretched workhouse the contrary prevails:
Does Age begin to prattle? – no man hearkens to his tales.

In a costly palace, if the child with a pin
Do but chance to prick a finger, straight the doctor is called in;
In a wretched workhouse, men are left to perish
For want of proper cordials,[3] which their old age might cherish

In a costly palace Youth enjoys his lust;
In a wretched workhouse, Age, in corners thrust,
Thinks upon the former days, when he was well to do,
Had children to stand by him, both friends and kinsmen too.

---

[1] *workhouse* – a place to house and 'employ' the poor and homeless
[2] *venison* – deer meat
[3] *cordials* – medicines

In a costly palace, Youth his temples hides
With a new devised peruke[4] that reaches to his sides;
In a wretched workhouse Age's crown is bare,
With a few thin locks just to fence out the cold air.

In peace, as in war, 'tis our young gallant's pride
To walk, each one, in the streets with a rapier[5] by his side,
That none to do them injury may have pretence;
Wretched Age, in poverty, must brook[6] offence.

[4] *peruke* – a type of wig
[5] *rapier* – a thin bladed sword used in fencing and duelling
[6] *brook* – tolerate

Holy Thursday

William Blake

Is this a holy thing to see,
In a rich and fruitful land,
Babes reduced to misery
Fed with cold and usurous[1] hand?

Is this trembling cry a song?
Can it be a song of joy?
And so many children poor?
It is a land of poverty!

And their sun does never shine.
And their fields are bleak and bare.
And their ways are fill'd with thorns
It is eternal winter there.

For where-e'er the sun does shine,
and where-e'er the rain does fall:
Babe can never hunger there,
Nor poverty the mind appall.

[1] *usurous* – a usurer is a money lender. Here it means that the 'babes' are fed by charities.

Sonnet: England in 1819

Percy Bysshe Shelley

An old, mad, blind, despised and dying king –
Princes, the dregs of their dull race, who flow
Through public scorn, mud from a muddy spring –
Rulers who neither see, nor feel, nor know,
But leech-like to their fainting country cling,
Till they drop, blind in blood, without a blow, –
A people starved and stabbed in the untilled field, –
An army, which liberticide[1] and prey
Make as an untilled field to all who wield, –
Golden and sanguine laws, which tempt and slay;
Religion Christless, Godless – a book sealed;
A Senate,[2] – Time's worst statute unrepealed, –
Are graves, from which a glorious Phantom[3] may
Burst to illumine our tempestuous day.

[1] *liberticide* – the act of destroying liberty and freedom
[2] *Senate* – the government
[3] *Phantom* – ghost

The Latest Decalogue

Arthur Hugh Clough

Thou shalt have one God only; who
would be at the expense of two?
No graven images may be
Worshipped, except the currency;
Swear not at all, for, for thy curse
Thine enemy is none the worse;
At church on Sunday to attend
Will serve to keep the world thy friend;
Honour thy parents; that is, all
From whom advancement may befall;
Thou shalt not kill, but need'st not strive
Officiously to keep alive;
Do not adultery commit;
Advantage rarely comes of it;
Thou shalt not steal; an empty feat,
When it's so lucrative to cheat;
Bear not false witness, let the lie
Have time on its own wings to fly;
Thou shalt not covet, but tradition
Approves all forms of competition.

The City

In a London Drawing Room

George Eliot

The sky is cloudy, yellowed by the smoke.
For view there are the houses opposite
Cutting the sky with one long line of wall
Like solid fog: far as the eye can stretch
Monotony of surface and of form
Without a break to hang a guess upon.
No bird can make a shadow as it lies,
For all its shadow, as in ways o'erhung
By thickest canvas, where the golden rays
Are clothed in hemp. No figure lingering
Pauses to feed the hunger of the eye
Or rest a little on the lap of life.
All hurry on and look upon the ground,
Or glance unmarking at passers by.
The wheels are hurrying too, cabs, carriages
All closed, in multiplied identity.
The world seems one huge prison house and court
Where men are punished at the slightest cost,
With lowest rate of colour, warmth and joy.

A Town Garden

Margaret Veley

A plot of ground the merest scrap
Deep like a dry, forgotten well,
A garden caught in a brick-built trap,
Where men make money, buy and sell;
And struggling through the stagnant haze
Dim flowers, with sapless leaf and stem,
Look up with something of the gaze
That homesick eyes have cast on them.

There is a rose against the wall,
With scanty, smoke-encrusted leaves,
Fair showers on happier roses fall
On this, foul droppings from the eaves.
It pines, but you need hardly note;
It dies by inches in the gloom;
Shoots in the spring time, as if by rote[1]
Long has forgotten to dream of bloom.

Could one transplant you (far on high
A murky sunset lights the tiles)
And set you 'neath the arching sky,
In the green country, many miles,
Would you strike deep and suck up strength
Washed with rain and hung with pearls,
Cling to the trellis, a leafy length,
Sweet with blossom for June and girls?

Yet no! Who needs you in these bowers[2]
Who prizes gifts that all can give?
Bestow your life instead of flowers,
And slowly die that dreams may live.
Prisoned and perishing, your dole
Of lingering leaves shall not be vain
Worthy to wreathe the hemlock[3] bowl
Or twine about the cross of pain![4]

[1] *by rote* – repeating until it is remembered
[2] *bowers* – shady places
[3] *hemlock* – a poisonous plant
[4] *cross of pain* Christ's crucifixion

London

William Blake

I wander thro' each charter'd[1] street
Near where the charter'd Thames does flow,
And mark in every face I meet
Marks of weakness, marks of woe.

In every cry of every Man,
In every Infant's cry of fear,
In every voice, in every ban,
The mind-forg'd manacles I hear.

How the Chimney-sweeper's cry
Every black'ning Church appalls,
And the hapless Soldier's sigh
Runs in blood down Palace walls.

But most thro' midnight streets I hear
How the youthful Harlot's curse
Blasts the new born Infant's tear,
And blights with plagues the Marriage hearse.

[1] *charter'd* – a charter given by the reigning monarch to a town or city to recognize their rights

Ballade of a Special Edition

Amy Levy

He comes. I hear him up the street
Bird of ill omen, flapping wide
The pinion of a printed sheet,
His hoarse note scares the eventide.
Of slaughter, theft and suicide
He is the herald and the friend;
Now he vociferates with pride
A double murder in Mile End.[1]

A hanging to his soul is sweet;
His gloating fancy's fain to bide
Where human freighted vessels meet,
And misdrected trains collide
With shocking accidents supplied.
He tramps the town from end to end.
How often have we heard it cried
A double murder in Mile End.

War loves he; victory or defeat,
So there be loss on either side
His tale of horrors incomplete,
Imagination's aid is tried
Since no distinguished man has died,
And since the Fates,[2] relenting, send
No great catastrophe, he's spied
This double murder in Mile End.

Fiend, get thee gone! No more repeat
Those sounds which do mine ears offend,
It is apocyrphal,[3] you cheat,
Your double murder in Mile End.

---

[1] *Mile End* – a poor part of London in Victorian times

[2] *Fates* – believed by the Greeks and Romans to decide the future

[3] *apocryphal* – made up or invented

Senses

Plum Blossoms

Chu Shu-Chen

The snow dances and the frost flies.
Through the bamboo blinds I see vaguely
The sparse shadows of slanting plum branches.
Unexpectedly a cold perfume,
Borne with the sound of a Tartar[1] flute;
Is blown to our bed curtains.
Enveloped in this puzzling scented wind,
Who can appreciate such subtle joy?
I quickly get up
In my dishevelled cloud dark hair.
We taste the stamens
And adorn ourselves with the blossoms,
Frowning and smiling,
Still drowsy with wine.

(translated from Chinese by Kenneth Rexroth and Ling Chung)

[1] *Tartar* – the Tartars were an Asiatic tribe with a reputation for being ferocious

Belinda's Toilet

Alexander Pope

And now, unveil'd, the *Toilet*[1] stands display'd
Each Silver Vase in mystic Order laid.
First, rob'd in White, the Nymph[2] intent adores
With Head uncover'd, the *Cosmetic* Pow'rs
A heav'nly Image in the Glass[3] appears,
To that she bends, to that her Eyes she rears;
Th'inferior Priestess, at her Altar's side,
Trembling, begins the sacred Rites of Pride.
Unnumber'd Treasures ope at once, and here
The various Off'rings of the World appear;
From each she nicely culls with curious Toil,
And decks the Goddess with the glitt'ring Spoil.
This Casket *India's* glowing Gems unlocks,
And all *Arabia* breathes from yonder Box.
The Tortoise here and Elephant unite,
Transform'd to *Combs*, the speckled and the white.
Here Files of Pins extend their shining Rows,
Puffs, Powders, Patches,[4] Bibles, Billet-doux.[5]
Now awful[6] Beauty puts on all its Arms;
The Fair each moment rises in her Charms,
Repairs her Smiles, awakens ev'ry Grace,
And calls forth all the Wonders of her Face;
Sees by Degrees a purer Blush arise,
And keener Lightnings quicken in her Eyes.

[1] *Toilet* – dressing table
[2] *Nymph* – a delicate and beautiful spirit (in Greek mythology).
[3] *Glass* – mirror
[4] *Patches* – a small piece of black silk worn on the face
[5] *Billet-doux* – love letters
[6] *awful* – powerful

Market Women's Cries

Jonathan Swift

Apples

Come buy my fine wares,
Plums, apples and pears.
A hundred a penny.
In conscience too many:
Come, will you have any?
My children are seven,
I wish them in Heaven;
My husband's a sot,
With his pipe and his pot,[1]
Not a farthing will gain them,
And I must maintain them.

Asparagus

Ripe 'sparagus
Fit for lad or lass,
To make their water pass:
O, 'tis pretty picking
With a tender chicken!

Onions

Come, follow me by the smell,
Here are delicate onions to sell;
I promise to use you well.
They make the blood warmer,
You'll feed like a farmer;
For this is every cook's opinion.
No savoury dish without an onion;
But, lest your kissing should be spoil'd,
Your onions must be thoroughly boil'd:
Or else you may spare
Your mistress a share,
The secret will never be known:
She cannot discover
The breath of her lover.
But think it as sweet as her own

---

[1] *pot* – beer mug

Oysters

Charming oysters I cry:
My masters, come by,
So plump and so fresh,
So sweet is their flesh,
No Colchester oyster
Is sweeter and moister:
Your stomach they settle,
They'll make you a dad
Of a lass or a lad;
And madam your wife
They'll please to the life;
Be she barren, be she old,
Be she slut or be she scold,
Eat my oysters, and lie near her,
She'll be fruitful, never fear.

Herrings

Be not sparing,
Leave off swearing.
Fresh of Malahide,[2]
Better never was tried.
Come, eat 'em with pure fresh butter and mustard,
Their bellies are soft, and as white as a custard.
Come, sixpence a-dozen, to get me some bread,
Or, like my own herrings, I soon shall be dead.

Oranges

Come buy my fine oranges, sauce for your veal,
And charming, when squeezed in a pot of brown ale;
Well roasted, with sugar and wine in a cup,
They'll make a sweet bishop when gentlefolks sup.

[2] *Malahide* – a town in Ireland

Reportage

Notes on England

Hippolyte Taine

Let us take a look at one of the reservoirs from which gold flows over the whole country and to all sorts and conditions of people – the London Docks.

First the tunnel: you go down a hundred steps, and from the bottom the hole looks as high as our Pantheon.[1] Five hundred paces long: it is a prodigious work, but, up to now, a folly serving no purpose. Little shops in the interior where children's toys are sold and a thin, tinkling music heard. Gas jets cast an unsteady light, the walls run with water: the thing is as enormous and dismal as the gut of some Babel.[2] I am always discovering that London resembles ancient Rome as Paris does Athens. How heavy must this modern Rome, as did the ancient one, bear down upon the backs of the working classes! . . . I have never looked upon a great city, a capital or a manufacturing town, without thinking of the nations about the Mediterranean which disappeared under the pressure of the Roman machine. True, there are nowadays no slaves *de jure;*[3] but in fact and by reason of the constraints of their station, men are often slaves.

These docks are prodigious, overwhelming; there are six of them, each a great port and each inhabited by a population of three-masted ships. Always ships, ships and more ships, lying side by side, showing the swelling lines of their prows, like handsome fishes, in their copper sheathing. One is from Australia and displaces 2500 tons; others are of 3000 or more, and they come from every corner of the world, for this is the whole world's meeting place . . .

Spices sector – hides and leather sector – fats and oils sector. Cellars and warehouses are colossal: beneath vaults equal in span to a mighty bridge, the crowded, busy dimness fades distantly into deep shadow: Rembrandt[4] would have found pictures ready-made in these mysterious perspectives, in the shifting darkness of these crammed and peopled cellars, in this infinity of store-rooms swarming with workers, like an ant-hill. They roll great bales and barrels calmly and without confusion. You hear the voices of clerks

---

[1] *Pantheon* – a temple dedicated to classical gods
[2] *Babel* – see Genesis Chapter 11 in The Bible. The tower of Babel from which came the sound of many voices talking in different languages
[3] de jure – according to the law
[4] *Rembrandt* – a Dutch artist in the Seventeenth Century

calling over numbers. In the middle of each cellar a 'foreman' sits at a small table, watching and making entries in a ledger. The masters, sober men in black hats walk about, supervise, say nothing. Meanwhile all about sounds the creaking of capstans and the noise of sailors scraping the hulls of their ships. So busied, dressed in working overalls, their expression serious, their faces phlegmatic or tired, they are pleasant to look upon; for one feels that they belong here and every living creature, animal or man, is a thing of beauty in his proper place.

I was seated on a bale, smoking, when a man who was passing said, without stopping, 'Five shillings fine!'

'Why, is it prohibited?'

'Yes.'

Nothing else. There is nothing better for action, or the promoting of action, than economy of words and gestures . . .

Near where I was is Shadwell, one of the poorest quarters. By the depths of its poverty and misery, as by its extent, it is proportional to London's enormous size and wealth. I have seen the lowest quarters of Marseilles, Antwerp, and Paris: they come nowhere near this. Squat houses, wretched streets of brick under red roofs crossing each other in all directions and leading dismally down to the river. Beggars, thieves, and prostitutes, especially the latter, swarm in Shadwell Street. The grating music from gin cellars can be heard from the street; sometimes the violinist is a negro, and through open windows one sees unmade beds and women dancing. Three times in ten minutes I saw crowds collect round doorways, attracted by fights, especially by fights between women . . .

A few of the women show vestiges of former cleanliness, or wear a new dress; but most of them are in dirty, ill-assorted rags. Imagine what a lady's hat can become after having passed for three or four years from one head to another, been dented against walls, bashed in by blows – for that happens frequently. I noticed numerous black eyes, bandaged noses, cut cheeks. These women gesticulate with extraordinary vehemence; but their most horrible attribute is the voice – thin, shrill, cracked, like that of a sick owl . . .

A passing tradesman warned me, 'Look out for your pockets, sir.' And a policeman advised me to keep out of certain 'lanes'.

I did, however, walk through several of the widest ones: all the houses, with one or two exceptions, were obviously inhabited by prostitutes. Other narrow alleys, and dusty yards, were foul with the smell of rotting, old clothes and decorated with rags and linen hung out to dry. There were swarms of children. At one time, in a narrow alley, I had fourteen or fifteen all round me, dirty, barefoot, one tiny girl carrying an infant, a baby still at breast but whose whitish head was completely bald. Nothing could be more dismal than these livid little bodies, the pale, stringy hair, the cheeks of flabby flesh encrusted with old filth. They kept running up, pointing out the 'gentleman' to each other with curious and avid gestures. Their mothers watched from doorways with dull, uninterested eyes. The interiors were visible, exiguous, sometimes a single room in which the family lives, breathing the foetid air. The houses are generally of a single storey, low, dilapidated, kennels to sleep and die in. What can it be like in winter when, during weeks of continuous rain and fog, the windows remain closed? And in order that each numerous brood shall not die of hunger, it is essential that the father abstain from drink, be never out of work, and never ill!

Here and there are rubbish dumps. Women work on them, sorting the rubbish for rags, bones, etc. One of them, old and wrinkled, had a short clay pipe in her mouth; they straightened up and stared at me from the midst of their muck-heap: dull, stupid, frightened faces of female yahoos.[5] Perhaps a pipe and a glass of gin is the last thought left in their idiot brains. Is it possible that anything but the instincts and appetites of a savage or a beast of burden can survive in them? A miserable black cat, emaciated, limping, half stupefied, was watching them fearfully out of one eye while furtively sniffing and pawing through a pile of rubbish; no doubt it was right to be nervous – the old woman was watching it with a look as bestial as its own, and mumbling, and it looked to me as if she were thinking that there went two pounds of meat.

I recall the lanes which open off Oxford Street, stifling alleys thick with human effluvia,[6] troops of pale children crouching on filthy staircases; the street benches at London Bridge where all night whole families huddle close, heads hanging, shaking with cold; above all I recall Haymarket and the Strand at evening, where you cannot walk a hundred yards without knocking into twenty streetwalkers: some of them ask you for a glass of gin; others say, 'It's for my rent, mister.' The impression is not one of debauchery but of abject, miserable poverty. One is sickened and wounded by this deplorable procession in those monumental streets. It seemed as if I were watching a march past of dead women. Here is a festering sore, the real sore on the body of English society.

[5] *yahoos* – the Yahoos are a primitive tribe in Jonathan Swift's *Gulliver's Travels*
[6] *effluvia* – a stream of particles carrying disease

Twelve Years a Slave

Solomon Northup

In the latter part of August begins the cotton picking season. At this time each slave is presented with a sack. A strap is fastened to it, which goes over the neck, holding the mouth of the sack breast high, while the bottom reaches nearly to the ground. Each one is also presented with a large basket that will hold about two barrels. This is to put the cotton in when the sack is filled. The baskets are carried to the field and placed at the beginning of the rows.

When a new hand, one unaccustomed to the business, is sent for the first time into the field, he is whipped up smartly, and made for that day to pick as fast as he can possibly. At night it is weighed, so that his capability in cotton picking is known. He must bring in the same weight each night following. If it falls short, it is considered evidence that he has been laggard, and a greater or less number of lashes is the penalty.

An ordinary day's work is considered two hundred pounds. A slave who is accustomed to picking, is punished, if he or she brings in a less quantity than that. There is a great difference among them as regards this kind of labour. Some of them seem to have a natural knack, or quickness, which enables them to pick with great celerity,[1] and with both hands, while others, with whatever practice or industry, are utterly unable to come up to the ordinary standard. Such hands are taken from the cotton field and employed in other business. Patsey, of whom I shall have more to say, was known as the most remarkable cotton picker on Bayou Boeuf. She picked with both hands and with such surprising rapidity, that five hundred pounds a day was not unusual for her.

Each one is tasked, therefore, according to his picking abilities, none, however, to come short of two hundred weight. I, being unskillful always in that business, would have satisfied my master by bringing in the latter quantity, while on the other hand, Patsey would surely have been beaten if she failed to produce twice as much.

The cotton grows from five to seven feet high, each stalk having a great many branches, shooting out in all directions, and lapping each other above the water furrow.

There are few sights more pleasant to the eye, than a wide cotton field when it is in the bloom. It presents an appearance of purity, like an immaculate expanse of light, new-fallen snow.

---

[1] *celerity* – speed

Sometimes the slave picks down one side of a row, and back upon the other, but more usually, there is one on either side, gathering all that has blossomed, leaving the unopened bolls for a succeeding picking. When the sack is filled, it is emptied into the basket and trodden down. It is necessary to be extremely careful the first time going through the field, in order not to break the branches off the stalks. The cotton will not bloom upon a broken branch. Epps never failed to inflict the severest chastisement on the unlucky servant who, either carelessly or unavoidably, was guilty in the least degree in this respect.

The hands are required to be in the cotton fields as soon as it is light in the morning, and, with the exception of ten or fifteen minutes, which is given them at noon to swallow their allowance of cold bacon, they are not permitted to be a moment idle until it is too dark to see, and when the moon is full, they often times labour till the middle of the night. They do not dare to stop even at dinner time, nor return to the quarters, however late it be, until the order to halt is given by the driver.

The day's work over in the field, the baskets are 'toted,' or in other words, carried to the gin-house,[2] where the cotton is weighed. No matter how fatigued and weary he may be – no matter how much he longs for sleep and rest – a slave never approaches the gin-house with his basket of cotton but with fear. If it falls short in weight – if he has not performed the full task appointed him, he knows that he must suffer. And if he has exceeded it by ten or twenty pounds, in all probability his master will measure the next day's task accordingly. So, whether he has too little or too much, his approach to the gin-house is always with fear and trembling. Most frequently they have too little, and therefore it is they are not anxious to leave the field. After weighing, follow the whippings; and then the baskets are carried to the cotton house, and their contents stored away like hay, all hands being sent in to tramp it down. If the cotton is not dry, instead of taking it to the gin-house at once, it is laid upon platforms, two feet high, and some three times as wide, covered with boards or plank, with narrow walks running between them.

This done, the labour of the day is not yet ended, by any means. Each one must then attend to his respective chores. One feeds the mules, another the swine – another cuts the wood, and so forth; besides, the packing is all done by candle light. Finally, at a late hour, they reach the quarters, sleepy and overcome with the long day's toil. Then a fire must be kindled in the cabin, the corn ground in the small hand-mill, and supper, and dinner for the next day in the field, prepared. All that is allowed them is corn and bacon, which is given out at the corncrib and smoke-house every Sunday morning. Each

[2] *gin-house* – a *gin* was a machine used for separating cotton from its seed

one receives, as his weekly allowance, three and a half pounds of bacon, and corn enough to make a peck of meal. That is all – no tea, coffee, sugar, and with the exception of a very scanty sprinkling now and then, no salt. I can say, from a ten years' residence with Master Epps, that no slave of his is ever likely to suffer from the gout, superinduced by excessive high living. Master Epps' hogs were fed on *shelled* corn – it was thrown out to his 'niggers', in the ear. The former, he thought, would fatten faster by shelling, and soaking it in the water – the latter, perhaps, if treated in the same manner, might grow too fat to labour. Master Epps was a shrewd calculator, and knew how to manage his own animals, drunk or sober.

The corn mill stands in the yard beneath a shelter. It is like a common coffee mill, the hopper holding about six quarts. There was one privilege which Master Epps granted freely to every slave he had. They might grind their corn nightly, in such small quantities as their daily wants required, or they might grind the whole week's allowance at one time, on Sundays, just as they preferred. A very generous man was Master Epps!

I kept my corn in a small wooden box, the meal in a gourd; and, by the way, the gourd is one of the most convenient and necessary utensils on a plantation. Besides supplying the place of all kinds of crockery in a slave cabin, it is used for carrying water to the fields. Another, also, contains the dinner. It dispenses with the necessity of pails, dippers, basins, and such tin and wooden superfluities altogether.

When the corn is ground, and fire is made, the bacon is taken down from the nail on which it hangs, a slice cut off and thrown upon the coals to broil. The majority of slaves have no knife, much less a fork. They cut their bacon with the axe at the woodpile. The corn meal is mixed with a little water, placed in the fire, and baked. When it is 'done brown', the ashes are scraped off, and being placed upon a chip, which answers for a table, the tenant of the slave hut is ready to sit down upon the ground to supper. By this time it is usually midnight. The same fear of punishment with which they approach the gin-house, possesses them again on lying down to get a snatch of rest. It is the fear of oversleeping in the morning. Such an offence would certainly be attended with not less than twenty lashes. With a prayer that he may be on his feet and wide awake at the first sound of the horn, he sinks to his slumbers nightly.

The softest couches in the world are not to be found in the log mansion of the slave. The one whereon I reclined year after year, was a plank twelve inches wide and ten feet long. My pillow was a stick of wood. The bedding was a coarse blanket, and not a rag or shred beside. Moss might be used, were it not that it directly breeds a swarm of fleas.

The cabin is constructed of logs, without floor or window. The latter is altogether unnecessary, the crevices between the logs admitting sufficient light. In stormy weather the rain drives through them, rendering it comfortless and extremely disagreeable. The rude door hangs on great wooden hinges. In one end is constructed an awkward fire-place.

An hour before day light the horn is blown. Then the slaves arouse, prepare their breakfast, fill a gourd with water, in another deposit their dinner of cold bacon and corn cake, and hurry to the field again. It is an offence invariably followed by a flogging, to be found at the quarters after daybreak. Then the fears and labours of another day begin; and until its close there is no such thing as rest. He fears he will be caught lagging through the day; he fears to approach the gin-house with his basket-load of cotton at night; he fears, when he lies down, that he will oversleep himself in the morning. Such is a true, faithful, unexaggerated picture and description of the slave's daily life, during the time of cotton-picking, on the shores of Bayou Boeuf.

In the month of January, generally, the fourth and last picking is completed. Then commences the harvesting of corn. This is considered a secondary crop, and receives far less attention than the cotton. It is planted, as already mentioned, in February. Corn is grown in that region for the purpose of fattening hogs and feeding slaves; very little, if any, being sent to market. It is the white variety, the ear of great size, and the stalk growing to the height of eight, and often times ten feet. In August the leaves are stripped off, dried in the sun, bound in small bundles, and stored away as provender[3] for the mules and oxen. After this the slaves go through the field, turning down the ear, for the purpose of keeping the rains from penetrating to the grain. It is left in this condition until after cotton-picking is over, whether earlier or later. Then the ears are separated from the stalks, and deposited in the corncrib with the husks on; otherwise, stripped of the husks, the weevil would destroy it. The stalks are left standing in the field.

The Carolina, or sweet potato, is also grown in that region to some extent. They are not fed, however, to hogs or cattle, and are considered but of small importance. They are preserved by placing them upon the surface of the ground, with a slight covering of earth or cornstalks. There is not a cellar on Bayou Boeuf. The ground is so low it would fill with water. Potatoes are worth from two to three 'bits,' or shillings a barrel; corn, except when there is an unusual scarcity, can be purchased at the same rate.

As soon as the cotton and corn crops are secured, the stalks are pulled up, thrown into piles and burned. The ploughs are started at the same time, throwing up the beds again, preparatory to another planting. The soil, in the parishes of Rapides and Avopelles, and throughout the whole country, so far as my observation extended, is of exceeding richness and fertility. It is

[3] *provender* – animal fodder

a kind of marl, of a brown or reddish colour. It does not require those invigorating composts necessary to more barren lands, and on the same field the same crop is grown for many successive years.

Ploughing, planting, picking cotton, gathering the corn, and pulling and burning stalks, occupies the whole of the four seasons of the year. Drawing and cutting wood, pressing cotton, fattening and killing hogs, are but incidental labours.

In the month of September or October, the hogs are run out of the swamps by dogs, and confined in pens. On a cold morning, generally about New Year's day, they are slaughtered. Each carcass is cut into six parts, and piled one above the other in salt, upon large tables in the smoke-house. In this condition it remains a fortnight, when it is hung up, and a fire built, and continued more than half the time during the remainder of the year. This thorough smoking is necessary to prevent the bacon from becoming infested with worms. In so warm a climate it is difficult to preserve it, and very many times myself and my companions have received our weekly allowance of three pounds and a half, when it was full of these disgusting vermin.

In Morocco

Edith Wharton

Whoever would understand Marrakech must begin by mounting at sunset to the roof of the Bahia.

Outspread below lies the oasis-city of the south, flat and vast as the great nomad camp it really is, its low roof extending on all sides to a belt of blue palms ringed with desert. Only two or three minarets and a few noblemen's houses among gardens break the general flatness; but they are hardly noticeable, so irresistibly is the eye drawn towards two dominant objects – the white wall of the Atlas[1] and the red tower of the Koutoubya.

Foursquare, untapering, the great tower lifts its flanks of ruddy stone. Its large spaces of unornamented wall, its triple tier of clustered openings, lightening as they rise from the severe rectangular lights of the first stage to the graceful arcade below the parapet, have the stern harmony of the noblest architecture. The Koutoubya would be magnificent anywhere; in this flat desert it is grand enough to face the Atlas . . .

. . . Marrakech [is] a city of Berbers and blacks and the last outpost against the fierce black world beyond the Atlas from which its founders came. When one looks at its site, and considers its history, one can only marvel at the height of civilization it attained.

The Bahia itself, now the palace of the Resident-General, though built less than a hundred years ago, is typical of the architectural megalomania of the great southern chiefs. . . They came, they built the Bahia, and it remains the loveliest and most fantastic of Moroccan palaces.

Court within court, garden beyond garden, reception halls, private apartments, slaves' quarters, sunny prophets' chambers on the roofs and baths in vaulted crypts, the labyrinth of passages and rooms stretches away over several acres of ground. A long court enclosed in pale-green trellis-work, where pigeons plume themselves about a great tank and the dripping tiles glitter with refracted sunlight, leads to the fresh gloom of a cypress garden, or under jasmine tunnels bordered with running water; and these again open on arcaded apartments faced with tiles and stucco-work,[2] where, in languid twilight, the hours drift by to the ceaseless music of the fountains.

---

[1] *the Atlas* – a mountain range in North Africa
[2] *stucco-work* – a fine plaster used for decorating walls and ceilings

The beauty of Moroccan palaces is made up of details of ornament and refinements of sensuous delight too numerous to record; but to get an idea of their general character it is worthwhile to cross the Court of Cypresses at the Bahia and follow a series of low-studded passages that turn on themselves till they reach the centre of the labyrinth. Here, passing by a low padlocked door leading to a crypt, and known as the 'Door of the Vizier's Treasure-House,' one comes on a painted portal that opens into a still more secret sanctuary: the apartment of the Grand Vizier's Favourite.

This lovely prison, from which all sight and sound of the outer world are excluded, is built about an atrium[3] paved with discs of turquoise and black and white. Water trickles from a central *vasca*[4] of alabaster into a hexagonal mosaic channel in the pavement. The walls, which are at least 25 feet high, are roofed with painted beams resting on panels of traceried stucco in which is set a clerestory[5] of jewelled glass. On each side of the atrium are long recessed rooms closed by vermillion doors painted with gold arabesques and vases of spring flowers; and into these shadowy inner rooms, spread with rugs and divans and soft pillows, no light comes except when their doors are opened into the atrium. In this fabulous place it was my good luck to be lodged while I was in Marrakech.

In a climate where, after the winter snow has melted from the Atlas, every breath of air for long months is a flame of fire, these enclosed rooms in the middle of the palaces are the only places of refuge from the heat. Even in October the temperature of the Favourite's apartment was deliciously reviving after a morning in the bazaars or the dusty streets, and I never came back to its wet tiles and perpetual twilight without the sense of plunging into a deep sea-pool.

From far off, through circuitous corridors, came the scent of citron-blossom and jasmine, with sometimes a bird's song before dawn, sometimes a flute's wail at sunset, and always the call of the muezzin[6] in the night; but no sunlight reached the apartment except in remote rays through the clerestory, and no air except through one or two broken panes.

Sometimes, lying on my divan, and looking out through the vermillion doors, I used to surprise a pair of swallows dropped down from their nest in the cedar-beams to preen themselves on the fountain's edge or in the channels of the pavement; for the roof was full of birds who came and went through the broken panes of the clerestory. Usually they were my only visitors; but one morning just at daylight I was waked by a soft tramp of bare

---

[3] *atrium* – a central courtyard surrounded by buildings

[4] vasca – fountain

[5] *clerestory* – the upper row of windows

[6] *muezzin* – a Muslim crier who calls the hours of prayer from a tower

feet, and saw, silhouetted against the cream-coloured walls a procession of eight tall negroes in linen tunics, who filed noiselessly across the atrium like a moving frieze of bronze . . .

A cock crew, and they vanished . . . and when I made the mistake of asking what they had been doing in my room at that hour I was told (as though it were the most natural thing in the world) that they were the municipal lamp-lighters of Marrakech, whose duty it is to refill every morning the two hundred acetylene lamps lighting the Palace of the Resident-General. Such unforeseen aspects, in this mysterious city, do the most ordinary domestic functions wear.

THE BAZAARS

Marrakech is the great market of the south; and the south means not only the Atlas with its feudal chiefs and their wild clansmen, but all that lies beyond of heat and savagery: the Sahara of the veiled Touaregs, Dakka, Timbuctoo, Senegal and the Soudan . . .

In the bazaars all these peoples meet and mingle: cattle-dealers, olive growers, peasants from the Atlas, the Souss and the Draa. Blue Men of the Sahara, blacks from Senegal and the Soudan, coming in to trade with the wool-merchants, tanners, leather-merchants, silk-weavers, armourers, and makers of agricultural implements.

Dark, fierce and fanatical are these narrow *souks*[7] of Marrakech. They are mere mud lanes roofed with rushes, as in South Tunisia and Timbuctoo, and the crowds swarming in them are so dense that it is hardly possible, at certain hours, to approach the tiny raised kennels where the merchants sit like idols among their wares. One feels at once that something more than the thought of bargaining – dear as this is to the African heart – animates these incessantly moving throngs. The *souks* of Marrakech seem, more than any others, the central organ of a native life that extends far beyond the city walls into secret clefts of the mountains and far-off oases where plots are hatched and holy wars fomented – farther still, to yellow deserts whence negroes are secretly brought across the Atlas to that inmost recess of the bazaar where the ancient traffic in flesh and blood still surreptitiously goes on.

All these many threads of the native life, woven of greed and lust, of fetishism and fear and blind hate of the stranger, form in the *souks*, a thick network in which at times one's feet seem literally to stumble. Fanatics in sheep skins glowering from the guarded thresholds of the mosques, fierce tribesmen with inlaid arms in their belts and the fighters' tufts of wiry hair escaping from camel's-hair turbans, mad negroes standing stark naked in

---

[7] souks – markets

niches of the walls pouring down Soudanese incantations upon the fascinated crowd, consumptive Jews with pathos and cunning in their large eyes and smiling lips, lusty slave-girls with earthen oil-jars resting against swaying hips, almond-eyed boys leading fat merchants by the hand, and bare-legged Berber women, tattooed and insolently gay, trading their striped blankets or bags of dried roses and irises, for sugar, tea, or Manchester cottons – from all these hundreds of unknown and unknowable people, bound together by secret affinities, or intriguing against each other with secret hate, there emanated an atmosphere of mystery and menace more stifling than the smell of camels and spices and black bodies and smoking fry which hangs like a fog under the close roofing of the *souks* . . .

. . . One passes into the barbaric splendour of a *souk* hung with innumerable plumy bunches of floss silk – skeins of citron yellow, crimson, grasshopper green, and pure purple. This is the silk-spinners' quarter, and next to it comes that of the dyers, with great seething vats into which the raw silk is plunged, and ropes overhead where the rainbow masses are hung out to dry.

Another turn leads into the street of the metal workers and armourers, where the sunlight through the thatch flames on round flanks of beaten copper or picks out the silver bosses of ornate powder-flasks and pistols; and nearby is the *souk* of the ploughshares, crowded with peasants in rough Chleuh cloaks[8] who are waiting to have their archaic ploughs repaired, and that of the smiths, in an outer lane of mud huts where negroes squat in the dust and sinewy naked figures in tattered loin cloths bend over blazing coals. And here ends the maze of the bazaar.

[8] *Chleuh cloaks* – a short cloak, originally worn in ancient Greece

Drama

No Baggage Allowance

Lucian

(*Scene: The River Styx.*[1] **Charon,** *a scruffy old man with long white hair and a beard, has just brought a derelict-looking boat in to the shore, where a large number of dead men, under the supervision of* **Hermes,** *are queuing up to go on board.*)

Charon: (*After putting out the gangway*) Now listen to me. Here's the situation. You can see for yourselves how small my boat is. It's also a bit rotten and tends to leak a good deal. What's more, if it develops the slightest list, it's liable to capsize and go to the bottom. But there you are, all turning up at the same time, with any amount of luggage! Well, if you take all that stuff on board, I'm afraid you're going to wish you hadn't – especially those who can't swim!

Hermes: Then what are we supposed to do, if we want to get across?

Charon: I'll tell you. You'll have to leave all that junk on the shore, take off everything you've got on, and come aboard like that. I'll only just manage to squeeze you in even then. So will you see to it, Hermes? Don't let anyone on to the boat until he's undressed and, as I say, deposited his luggage. You'd better stand at the foot of the gangway and check them over. Make sure they take off everything before they embark.

Hermes: Very well, that's what I'll do. All right, who's first?

Man at the head of the queue: My name's Menippus. Well, there goes my stick – and my knapsack. (*He throws them into the water.*) As for my cloak, I took if off before I came – and how right I was!

Hermes: Good for you, Menippus! On you go. You can have the best seat, up there beside the rudder. Then you can keep an eye on the rest of the passengers.

(**Menippus** *goes on board and sits down.*)

And who's this gorgeous creature?

Next man in the queue: I'm Charmoleus, the beauty king from Megara, the boy with the million–dollar kiss.

---

[1] *River Styx* – over which, in Greek mythology, the dead had to travel to reach the Underworld

Hermes: Off with your beauty then. Off with your lips, kisses, and all. Off with that lovely long hair and those rosy cheeks – in fact off with your whole body . . . That's right, now you're travelling really light. You can go aboard now.

(*The skeleton of* **Charmoleus** *goes on board.*)

(*To the next man in the queue*) And who may you be, with your crown and purple robes and disagreeable expression?

Next man: I am Lampichus, King of Gelonia.

Hermes: Well, Lampichus, what do you think you're doing with all that paraphernalia?

Lampichus: You can hardly expect a king to travel in the nude.

Hermes: If he's a dead king certainly – I do. Take it all off.

Lampichus: (*Removing his jewellery*) There! I have jettisoned the Crown Jewels.

Hermes: You'd better jettison your conceit as well, Lampichus. A mass of arrogance like that will overload the boat.

Lampichus: Very well, but at least let me keep my crown and my royal robes.

Hermes: Certainly not. They must go too.

Lampichus: (*Taking them off*) All right. What else do you want? I've taken off everything, can't you see?

Hermes: Oh no, you haven't. There's still your cruelty, and your stupidity, and your insolence, and your bad temper. Off with them as well.

Lampichus: Here I am, then, stripped absolutely bare.

Hermes: Right. You can go on board now.

(**Lampichus** *goes on board.*)

And who is this great lump of flesh?

Next man: I'm Damasias, the famous heavy-weight champion.

Hermes: Yes. I suppose you must be. I know I've often seen you in the ring.

Damasias: (*Complacently*) I expect you have, Hermes. Well, let me pass – I've got nothing on.

Hermes: Nothing on, my dear chap, when you're wearing all that flesh? For heaven's sake take it off, or you'll sink the boat the moment you set foot in it. And get rid of all those championships and all that publicity too.

Damasias: Take a look at me now, then. This time I'm really stripped and weigh no more than any of the others.

Hermes: Yes that's much better. It's always healthy to lose weight. On you go.

(*A powerfully-built skeleton goes on board.*)

Ah, Craton! I'm afraid you'll have to leave that money behind, and your luxury and effeminacy as well. You won't be able to bring that expensive shroud or that distinguished pedigree. You must say good-bye to rank and reputation and titles, and to all those flattering inscriptions on your statues. And you'll have to stop talking about the great tomb that they've built for you. The mere mention of such things would be enough to sink us.

Craton: It's a horrible wrench but – there they go. What else can one do?

(*He goes on board.*)

Hermes: (*To the next man, who is a soldier killed in action*) Hullo, what's the Army doing here? And what's that medal for?

Soldier: It's a decoration that I won for distinguished service in the field.

Hermes: You must throw it away. And you won't be needing any of that equipment either – it's always peacetime down here.

(*The soldier grounds arms, removes his medal and battledress, and goes on board.*)

And who is this dignified character with his nose in the air, a furrowed brow, an air of deep meditation, and a long, flowing beard?

Menippus: (*From his seat in the boat*) He's a philosopher, Hermes – or rather, that's what he pretends to be, but actually he's quite bogus. Make him undress too. You'll find some very funny things under his cloak.

Hermes: (*To the Philosopher*) Yes, let's have the cloak off first of all, and, then everything else.

(*The **Philosopher** removes his cloak.*)

Good God, look at all the imposture he's brought with him! Look at all that ignorance and conceit and quarrelsomeness – all those tricky questions and thorny problems and tortuous arguments – not to mention a fair amount of wasted effort, a good deal of nonsense, and a lot of fuss about nothing! But, my goodness, that's not all! Here's some money-grubbing too, and some sensuality and impudence and bad temper and luxury and debauchery. I can see it all, however much you try to conceal it. And here's some lying, and arrogance, and thinking oneself better than other people – they'll have to go too. Why, there'd hardly be room for all that luggage on an ocean-liner!

Philosopher: Well, I've done as you told me. It's all gone now.

Menippus: Hadn't he better take off that beard as well, Hermes! Just look how bushy it is. There must be at least five pounds of hair there.

Hermes: Quite right. (*To the Philosopher*) Take your beard off too.

Philosopher: Who can I get to shave if off for me?

Hermes: Menippus here will do it. He can spread it out on the gangway, and chop it off with an axe from the toolbox.

Menippus: (*Jumping up and opening the toolbox*) Oh, couldn't I use a saw instead, Hermes? It would be much more fun.

Hermes: No, an axe will do.

(**Menippus** *performs the operation.*)

(*To the* **Philosopher**) Yes, that's much better. Why, you look quite like a human being now, instead of a goat.

Menippus: (*Still fingering the axe*) Would you like me to take a little off his eyebrows too?

Hermes: Yes, please. He keeps knitting them and raising them in a most supercilious way – I can't think why.

(*The* **Philosopher** *starts crying.*)

What's the matter now, you wretched creature? What are you snivelling for? Are you afraid you might get killed? Oh, all right, go on board as you are.

(**Menippus** *replaces the axe and returns to his seat. The* **Philosopher** *starts walking up the gangway.*)

Menippus: I say, he's still got something tucked away under his arm and it's the most depressing thing about him.

Hermes: Oh? And what's that, Menippus?

Menippus: Flattery, Hermes. He's always found it very useful in the past.

Philosopher: (*Now safe in the boat*) Well, what about you, Menippus? Hadn't you better leave your frankness behind, and your equanimity, and your courage, and your sense of humour? For you're the only one of us that ever laughs.

Hermes: (*To* **Menippus**) Don't you do anything of the kind. You hang on to them – they're all quite buoyant, and will help to keep us afloat. (*To the next man*) And you, I suppose, are a public speaker? Well, you'll have to drop that great mass of verbiage, all those antitheses and parallelisms and perorations and solecisms[2] – in fact the whole of that ponderous style of yours.

Public Speaker: There they go, then.

(*He goes on board.*)

Hermes: (*To* **Charon**) All right, skipper, you can cast off now. In with the gangway, up with the anchor, hoist sail, and man the rudder! Off we go, and good luck to us!

(*As the boat begins to move the passengers raise a wail of despair.*)

What's the matter now, you silly creatures? Most of the noise seems to be coming from that philosopher who's just had his beard demolished. (*To the* **Philosopher**) Well, what's your trouble?

Philosopher: (*Sobbing*) It's just that I always thought the soul was immortal, Hermes.

Menippus: (*To* **Hermes**) Don't you believe it. If you ask me, he's got something very different on his mind.

Hermes: Oh? What?

Menippus: He can't bear to think of never having another expensive dinner, and then sneaking out late at night with his cloak pulled up over his face and going the round of the brothels – and next morning extracting large sums of money from young men under the false pretence of teaching them wisdom!

Philosopher: Well, how about you, Menippus? Aren't you at all upset at being dead?

(*A confused uproar is heard in the distance.*)

Menippus: Of course not. Why, I came here of my own accord. I wasn't even invited. But didn't you hear a noise just then, as if people were shouting in the world behind us?

Hermes: Certainly we did, Menippus, and it came from several different places. First of all they've called a public meeting in Gelonia,

[2] *antitheses . . . parallelisms . . . perorartions . . . solecisms* – all speech-making (rhetorical) techniques

and everyone's roaring with laughter at the news that King Lampichus is dead. His wife's being lynched by the women, and the children are throwing stones at her new-born babies. Then in Sicyon Diophantus has just got a round of applause for his funeral oration over Craton here.

(*A piercing shriek is heard.*)

And, my goodness, that was Damasias's mother starting of the keening over his body. But nobody's mourning for you, Menippus. You're lying there quite peacefully, all by yourself.

Menippus: Don't you believe it. Any minute now you'll hear the dogs howling over me in the most heart-broken manner, and the crows beating their breasts with their wings, when they all turn up for my funeral.

Hermes: That's the spirit, Menippus. Well, here we are on the other side. Off you all go to the Last Judgement. It's straight along that path there. (*He points into the semi-darkness.*) Meanwhile Charon and I will go back for some more passengers.

Menippus: (*Getting up and moving towards Charon, who is putting out the gangway*) Have a good trip then, Hermes. Come along, the rest of you.

(*The passengers remain trembling in their seats.*)

It's no use, we've all got to stand our trial – and I'm told the sentences are pretty stiff and liable to involve such things as wheels, stones, and vultures. And all the secrets of our private lives are going to come out.

Macbeth

William Shakespeare

ACT 2 SCENE 3

Introduction: this scene follows the death of King Duncan who has been murdered in his bed in the night by Macbeth while the king was visiting him. Macbeth was encouraged to commit the murder by his wife, Lady Macbeth. The scene opens with Macbeth greeting Lennox who has come to escort the king away from Macbeth's castle the following morning. At this point only Macbeth and Lady Macbeth know that the king is dead.

Lennox: Good morrow, noble sir.

Macbeth: Good morrow, both.

Macduff: Is the king stirring, worthy thane?

Macbeth: Not yet.

Macduff: He did command me to call timely on him:
    I have almost slipp'd[1] the hour.

Macbeth: I'll bring you to him.

Macduff: I know this is a joyful trouble to you;
    But yet 'tis one.

Macbeth: The labour we delight in physics[2] pain.
    This is the door.

Macduff: I'll make so bold to call,
    For 'tis my limited service. *(Exit)*

Lennox: Goes the king hence to-day?

Macbeth: He does: he did appoint so.

Lennox: The night has been unruly: where we lay,
    Our chimneys, were blown down; and, as they say,
    Lamentings heard i' the air; strange screams of death,
    And prophesying with accents terrible
    Of dire combustion and confus'd events
    New hatch'd to the woeful time. The obscure[3] bird
    Clamour'd the livelong night: some say the earth
    Was feverous and did shake.

Macbeth: 'Twas a rough night.

Lennox: My young remembrance cannot parallel
    A fellow to it.

---

[1] *slipp'd* – missed

[2] *physics* – cures

[3] *obscure* – the owl which flies in the dark (obscure)

(*Re-enter* **Macduff**.)

Macduff: O horror! horror! horror! Tongue nor heart
Cannot conceive nor name thee!
Macbeth:⎫
Lennox:⎭   What's the matter?
Macduff: Confusion now hath made his masterpiece!
Most sacrilegious murder hath broke ope[4]
The Lord's anointed temple,[5] and stole thence
The life o' the building!
Macbeth: What is 't you say? the life?
Lennox: Mean you his majesty?
Macduff: Approach the chamber, and destroy your sight
With a new Gorgon:[6] do not bid me speak;
See, and then speak yourselves.

(*Exeunt* **Macbeth** *and* **Lennox**.)

                    Awake! Awake!
Ring the alarum-bell. Murder and treason!
Banquo and Donalbain! Malcolm, awake!
Shake off this downy sleep, death's counterfeit,[7]
And look on death itself! Up, up, and see
The great doom's image! Malcolm! Banquo!
As from your graves rise up, and walk like sprites,
To countenance[8] this horror! Ring the bell.

(*Bell rings.*)

(*Enter* **Lady Macbeth**)

Lady Macbeth: What's the business,
That such a hideous trumpet calls to parley[9]
The sleepers of the house? Speak!
Macduff: O gentle lady!
'Tis not for you to hear what I can speak;
The repetition in a woman's ear
Would murder as it fell.

---

[4] *ope* – open
[5] *The Lord's anointed temple* – the King, who was anointed with Holy oil when crowned
[6] *Gorgon* – a monster said to turn men to stone if they looked at it (in Greek mythology).
[7] *death's counterfeit* – sleep, because it is like being dead
[8] *countenance* – look at
[9] *parley* – tell

(*Enter* **Banquo**.)

                                    O Banquo! Banquo!
Our royal master's murder'd!
Lady Macbeth: Woe, alas!
  What! in our house?
Banquo: Too cruel anywhere.
  Dear Duff, I prithee, contradict thyself,
  And say it is not so.

(*Enter* **Macbeth** *and* **Lennox**.)

Macbeth: Had I but died an hour before this chance,
  I had liv'd a blessed time; for, from this instant,
  There's nothing serious in mortality,
  All is but toys; renown and grace is dead,
  The wine of life[10] is drawn, and the mere lees
  Is left this vault to brag of.

(*Enter* **Malcolm** *and* **Donalbain**.)

Donalbain: What is amiss?
Macbeth: You are, and do not know't:
  The spring, the head, the fountain of your blood
  Is stopp'd; the very source of it is stopp'd.
Macduff: Your royal father's murder'd.
Malcolm: O! by whom?
Lennox: Those of his chamber, as it seem'd, had done 't:
  Their hands and faces were all badg'd with blood;
  So were their daggers, which unwip'd we found
  Upon their pillows: they star'd, and were distracted;
  No man's life was to be trusted with them.
Macbeth: O yet I do repent me of my fury,
  That I did kill them.
Macduff: Wherefore did you so?
Macbeth: Who can be wise, amaz'd, temperate and furious,
  Loyal and neutral, in a moment? No man.
  The expedition of my violent love

---

[10] *The wine of life* – Macbeth is comparing life to a wine-cellar – vault – from which, now
that the King is dead, the best wine has been taken, leaving only the dregs – the lees – behind

Outran the pauser, reason.[11] Here lay Duncan,
His silver skin lac'd with his golden blood;
And his gash'd stabs look'd like a breach in nature,
For ruin's wasteful entrance:[12] there, the murderers,
Steep'd in the colours of their trade, their daggers
Unmannerly breech'd with gore:[13] who could refrain,
That had a heart to love and in that heart
Courage to make 's love known?

Lady Macbeth: Help me hence, ho!

Macduff: Look to the lady.

Malcolm: (*Aside to* **Donalbain**) Why do we hold our tongues,
That most may claim this argument for ours?

Donalbain: (*Aside to* **Malcolm**) What should be spoken
Here where our fate, hid in an auger-hole,
May rush and seize us? Let's away: our tears
Are not yet brew'd.

Malcolm: (*Aside to* **Donalbain**) Nor our strong sorrow
Upon the foot of motion.

Banquo: Look to the Lady:

(**Lady Macbeth** *is carried out.*)

And when we have our naked frailties hid,[14]
That suffer in exposure, let us meet,
And question this most bloody piece of work,
To know it further. Fears and scruples shake us:
In the great hand of God I stand, and thence
Against the undivulg'd pretence[15] I fight
Of treasonous malice.

Macduff: And so do I.

All: So all.

Macbeth: Let's briefly put on manly readiness,
And meet i' the hall together.

All: Well contented.

---

[11] *the pauser, reason* – reason or thinking is what makes us consider, or pause, in our actions
[12] *a breach in nature . . . ruin's wasteful entrance* – Macbeth describes the stab wounds which
have destroyed the King's life by entering his body
[13] *Unmannerly breech'd with gore* – Macbeth describes the murderers as being clothed –
breech'd – with blood – gore
[14] *our naked frailties hid* – dressed
[15] *undivulg'd pretence* – a secret plot

She Stoops to Conquer

Oliver Goldsmith

ACT 2 SCENE 1

Introduction: this scene takes place in a large country house. Mr Hastings is a fashionable young man from London. He has been telling Mrs Hardcastle about life in the big city. Throughout the scene Mr Hastings is pretending to be impressed with Mrs Hardcastle's attempts at being fashionable.

Mrs Hardcastle: Well! I vow, Mr Hastings, you are very entertaining. There's nothing in the world I love to talk of so much as London, and the fashions, though I was never there myself.

Hastings: Never there! You amaze me! From your air and manner, I concluded you had been bred all your life either at Ranelagh, St James', or Tower Wharf.[1]

Mrs Hardcastle: Oh! Sir, you're only pleased to say so. We country persons can have no manner at all. I'm in love with the town, and that serves to raise me above some of our neighbouring rustics; but who can have a manner, that has never seen the Pantheon, the Grotto Gardens, the Borough,[2] and such places where the Nobility chiefly resort? All I can do, is to enjoy London at second-hand. I take care to know every tête-à-tête from the *Scandalous Magazine*,[3] and have all the fashions, as they come out, in a letter from the two Miss Rickets of Crooked Lane. Pray how do you like this head, Mr Hastings?

Hastings: Extremely elegant and *dégagée*,[4] upon my word, madam, Your *Friseur*[5] is a Frenchman, I suppose?

Mrs Hardcastle: I protest I dressed it myself from a print in the *Ladies Memorandum-book*[6] for the last year.

[1] *Ranelagh, St James', or Tower Wharf* – the first two were fashionable places in London but Tower Wharf was not. In saying this, Hastings is laughing at Mrs Hardcastle's ignorance of the difference between these places.

[2] *Pantheon, the Grotto Gardens, the Borough* – Mrs Hardcastle shows how out of date her knowledge of London was because only the Pantheon was visited by the 'Nobility' when this play was written

[3] *tête-à-tête from the* Scandalous Magazine – Mrs Hardcastle reads about the gossip and scandal in fashionable London society from magazines

[4] dégagée – free and easy

[5] Friseur – hairdresser

[6] Ladies Memorandum-book – contained fashionable ideas for hair styles

Hastings: Indeed. Such a head in a side-box,[7] at the Playhouse, would draw as many gazers as my Lady Mayoress at a City Ball.

Mrs Hardcastle: I vow, since inoculation[8] began, there is no such thing to be seen as a plain woman; so one must dress a little particular or one may escape in the crowd.

Hastings: But that can never be your case, madam, in any dress.

(*Bowing*)

Mrs Hardcastle: Yet, what signifies *my* dressing when I have such a piece of antiquity by my side as Mr Hardcastle: all I can say will never argue down a single button from his clothes. I have often wanted him to throw off his great flaxen wig, and where he was bald, to plaster it over like my Lord Pately, with powder.

Hastings: You are right, madam; for, as among the ladies, there are none ugly, so among the men there are none old.

Mrs Hardcastle: But what do you think his answer was? Why, with his usual Gothic[9] vivacity, he said I only wanted him to throw off his wig to convert it into a *tête*[10] for my own wearing.

Hastings: Intolerable! At your age you may wear what you please, and it must become you.

Mrs Hardcastle: Pray, Mr Hastings, what do you take to be the most fashionable age about town?

Hastings: Some time ago, forty was all the mode;[11] but I'm told the ladies intend to bring up fifty for the ensuing winter.

Mrs Hardcastle: Seriously! Then I shall be too young for the fashion.

Hastings: No lady begins now to put on jewels till she's past forty. For instance, Miss there, in a polite circle, would be considered as a child, as a mere maker of samplers.[12]

Mrs Hardcastle: And yet Mrs Niece thinks herself as much a woman, and is as fond of jewels as the oldest of us all.

Hastings: Your niece, is she? And that young gentleman, a brother of yours, I should presume?

[7] *side-box* – separate seating at the theatre, at the side of the stage. These were seats that could be seen by the rest of the audience

[8] *inoculation* – against smallpox. Like all her other attempts to impress Mr Hastings, she is out of date. This type of inoculation had been common for about fifty years.

[9] *Gothic* – Mrs Hardcastle uses this word to mean out of fashion

[10] tête – a built-up hair piece, like a wig, worn by women

[11] *mode* – fashion

[12] *sampler* – a small piece of embroidery, to show a range of stitches

Mrs Hardcastle: My son, sir. They are contracted to each other. Observe their little sports. They fall in and out ten times a day, as if they were man and wife already. (*To them*) Well Tony, child, what soft things are you saying to your cousin Constance this evening?

Tony: I have been saying no soft things; but that it's very hard to be followed about so. Ecod![13] I've not a place in the house now that's left to myself but the stable.

Mrs Hardcastle: Never mind him, Con my dear. He's in another story behind your back.

Miss Neville: There's something generous in my cousin's manner. He falls out before faces to be forgiven in private.

Tony: That's a damned confounded—crack.[14]

Mrs Hardcastle: Ah! he's a sly one. Don't you think they're like each other about the mouth, Mr Hastings? The Blenkinsop mouth to a T.[15] They're of a size too. Back to back, my pretties, that Mr Hastings may see you. Come Tony.

Tony: You had as good not make me, I tell you.

(*Measuring*)

Miss Neville: O lud![16] he has almost cracked my head.

Mrs Hardcastle: Oh the monster! For shame, Tony. You a man, and behave so!

Tony: If I'm a man, let me have my fortin. Ecod! I'll not be made a fool of no longer.

Mrs Hardcastle: Is this, ungrateful boy, all that I'm to get for the pains I have taken in your education? I that have rocked you in your cradle, and fed that pretty mouth with a spoon! Did not I work[17] that waistcoat to make you genteel? Did not I prescribe for you every day, and weep while the receipt[18] was operating?

---

[13] *Ecod* – By God
[14] *crack* – lie
[15] *to a T* – exactly
[16] *O lud!* – Oh Lord!
[17] *work* – embroider
[18] *receipt* – a medicine

Tony: Ecod! you had reason to weep, for you have been dosing me ever since I was born. I have gone through every receipt in the *Complete Huswife*[19] ten times over; and you have thoughts of coursing me through *Quincy*[19] next spring. But, ecod! I tell you, I'll not be made a fool of no longer.

Mrs Hardcastle: Wasn't it all for your good, viper? Wasn't it all for your good?

---

[19] Complete Huswife . . . Quincy . . . – the names of two popular magazines offering helpful household tips

The Government Inspector

Nikolai Gogol

ACT I

Introduction: this scene takes place in a small town in Russia. All the characters have official positions in the town.

(*A room in the Mayor's house; the furnishings are approximately Empire, very varied, and reveal some lack of taste; up centre are folding doors, the usual entry; up right a door leading to a bedroom, and right a window, which is practical; up left is a door leading to the rest of the house; there is no open fireplace, but a Russian stove on the wall, left; this looks like a large cabinet or wardrobe, without legs, and warms the room by the heat from its walls; it is painted to represent enamel and is in use, as it is winter; there is a chandelier and also candelabra here and there, but these are only illuminated in Act 1 and Act 3, Sc. 1; there is a sofa, a table, and numerous chairs. It is morning, about 8 o'clock. At curtain rise the* **Judge**, *the* **Charity Commissioner**, *and the* **School Superintendent** *are discovered, in various attitudes of waiting; they should convey a feeling of uneasy anticipation; the* **Judge** *is sprawling in a chair and for him and* **Hlopov** *this is clearly 'the morning after'; he strives to focus on his watch but cannot manage it;* **Hlopov** *paces nervously; his dress has been rather hastily put on; the* **Charity Commissioner** *stands by the window with a more confident air, but even he, like the others, glances uneasily now and then at the door, left. Enter the* **Mayor**; *he is in uniform; the* **Judge** *rises at once and all three pay respectful attention.*)

Mayor: (*Briskly*) Good morning, gentlemen. I asked you here this morning because I have some very unpleasant news for you. I have found out that an Inspector-General is coming from Petersburg with secret orders to inspect our province, and especially everything to do with our district. He will travel incognito.

Judge: What are you saying? From Petersburg?

Charity Commissioner: With secret orders?

School Superintendent: And incognito!

Mayor: I don't like the business any better than you do. But, you know, I had a premonition of it. I was dreaming all last night about two enormous rats! Upon my soul, I never saw such brutes, huge black ones! They came, sniffed, and went away again! But I'll read you the letter I've just had from Tchmihov; (*to Charity Commissioner*) You know him, Artémy Filípovitch. He writes: 'Dear friend, godfather, and benefactor

(*He mutters under his breath, eyes moving swiftly*) Ah! This is it: ' . . . and I hasten to warn you that an official is coming to inspect the whole province, and especially our district. I have learned this from an absolutely trustworthy source, although the man passes himself off as a private person. I know you are like all the rest of us and have your little failings, for being a sensible fellow you don't like to lose what swims into your hands.' (*Disconcerted, but looks up saying*) Oh well, we're all friends here. 'I warn you to take precautions, as he may arrive any moment, if he hasn't already arrived and is living somewhere incognito. The other day I . . .' The rest is only about family matters, 'my cousin A'nna Kirílovna and her husband are staying with us. He has got very stout and is always playing the fiddle,' and so on, and so on. Well, there you are, gentlemen.

Judge: But it's extraordinary, simply extraordinary!

School Superintendent: Tell me please, Antón Antónovitch, why this has happened. Why send an Inspector to us? Our town is so far away. Why should they care about us?

Mayor: Why? It must be fate. Up to now, God has been good to us, they've pried into other towns; we never had anything like this. Well now, it's our turn.

Judge: I believe, Antón Antónovitch, there's some deep, far reaching political reason for this. I have it! Russia is going to war, and the Ministry has sent this man to find out . . . Yes! To find out if there is treason anywhere!

Mayor: What next? And you an intelligent man! Treason in a country town! Is this the frontier? You could gallop from here for three years and not reach a foreign country!

Judge: No, you're wrong. Petersburg may be far away, but the authorities don't miss much. They see everything!

Mayor: (*Uneasily*) Well, they may, or they may not, that doesn't matter now. This inspector may even now be undoing us all behind our own backs. As to my own special responsibilities, the police, and the general good order of the town, I have already taken some steps, and I advise you to do the same. (*Swinging round on Charity Commissioner*) Especially you, Artémy Filípovitch; this official will certainly inspect your institutions, and you had better see they look decent! Get some clean nightcaps and bedclothes, the ones you've got are enough for a report in themselves. And the patients might look a little less like chimney sweeps!

Charity Commissioner: That's nothing much. I may be able to find some clean nightcaps.

Mayor: And there ought to be some way of distinguishing the patients. Put a sign over each bed, and get the doctor to put up, in Latin or some such language, the names of the patients when admitted, their diseases, and so on. And make them stop smoking that filthy tobacco for a while, it makes me choke whenever I go in! And get rid of some of the patients; there are far too many. He'll think the doctor doesn't know his business!

Charity Commissioner: Oh! The doctor and I have got things well arranged in the medical line. The more natural your treatment is, the better. We don't bother with expensive medicines! These patients are very simple people! If they die, well! they die! If they get better, they get better! And it would really be very difficult for Hiebner to talk to them. He's a very good doctor, but he doesn't know a word of Russian!

Mayor: (*To Judge*) And you ought to do something about the state of your courthouse, A'mmos Fydórovitch! Your porter keeps geese in the anterooms, and goslings, and they run about and peck under your feet. Of course it's a good thing to keep poultry, very praiseworthy, but can't he keep them somewhere else? It makes the place smell so!

Judge: That's a small matter. I can have them killed today. Would you like to come to dinner tonight?

Mayor: Then your offices are full of all kinds of rubbish. Skins hanging up to dry, and whips and gear mixed up with the papers. I know you're very fond of hunting, but why not tidy it up till this inspector's been, then you can put it all back, if you want to! Then that clerk of yours! He may know a great deal, but he gives off a powerful odour of vodka! I've wanted to talk these things over with you for some time, but something has always turned up to put it out of my mind. If it really is his natural smell, as he says it is, there must be a remedy. Tell him to try eating onions, or perhaps the doctor could give him something or other.

Judge: No, it's no good. He says when he was a child his nurse bruised him, and he's given off a slight smell of vodka ever since.

Mayor: Well, I thought I'd mention it. About your conduct in Court, and what Tchmihov in his letter calls 'little failings' well! What is there to say? No man is without sin. It's God's will, and it is no use the free-thinkers arguing about it.

Judge: Well, there are sins and sins. I freely admit I take bribes, but what sort of bribes? Borzoi puppies, that's all!

Mayor: Whether it's Borzoi puppies or something else, it's still bribery.

Judge: But you're wrong there. For example, if a man takes a fur coat, worth 500 roubles, or a shawl for his wife . . .

Mayor: (*Who doesn't relish this line*) Well, what of it? Only taking puppies as bribes won't save you. Why, you don't believe in God! You never go to church! As for me, I do at least believe devoutly, and I go to church every Sunday. But you . . . when you start talking about the creation of the world, it makes my hair stand on end!

Judge: Well, at least my opinions are my own. A man who thinks for himself . . .

Mayor: Sometimes much thinking is worse than none at all. As for the rest, I only mentioned about the district courthouse, but to tell the truth, hardly anyone is likely to look into it. It's in such a state, it must be under divine protection. (*Wheeling round*) Now then, Luká Lúkitch, as the school superintendent it's your business to superintend the teachers. I know they're very learned men, educated in all kinds of colleges, but their behaviour is most peculiar. Perhaps that's the natural way of educated men, I don't know. There's one who's always making grimaces. He might put this Inspector in a very bad mood.

School Superintendent: What can I do? I did speak to him about it once; it was the day the prince inspected us. That man pulled such a fearful face, I never saw anything like it! I got a telling-off for letting the boys be taught wild, godless ideas!

Mayor: Yes, yes. Now take the history teacher. He's an able chap, knows his subject, but he expounds it with so much heat, that there's no understanding him. I listened to him once; while he was talking about the Assyrians and Babylonians, he was all right, but when he came to Alexander the Great, it was simply indescribable! I thought the place was on fire! He jumped down from his desk, took a chair and banged it on the floor, brandished it over his head! I think he was describing a battle. Now Alexander the Great was a great general and all that, but why break the chairs, they're Government property?

School Superintendent: Yes, he's a hothead. I've spoken to him about it, but he just says, 'As you wish, but I would lay down my life in the cause of learning!'

Mayor: Yes, it's a mysterious law of life. Clever men are never quite sane. They either drink, or go mad and make faces that would shock the saints!

School Superintendent: Heaven help any man in the education line! These clever fellows put me in a sweat whenever they open their mouths! Always showing off!

Mayor: It wouldn't matter but . . . it's the cursed incognito! He may look in any minute and say, 'Aha, My pets! Here you are! And who is Health Commissioner here? Zemlyaníka. Hand over Zemlyaníka! And who is the judge? Lyápkin-Tyápkin. Hand over Lyápkin-Tyápkin.' It's awful!

(*The door opens; all jump; the* **Postmaster** *comes in.*)

Postmaster: Tell me; what's this about an Inspector, gentlemen?

Mayor: Have you only just heard?

Postmaster: I heard something from Peter Ivánovitch Bóbchinsky. He's just been to see me at the post office.

Mayor: What's your opinion?

Postmaster: I think it means war with the Turks.

Judge: Just what I said! My very words!

Postmaster: Yes! It's all the fault of those filthy French!

Mayor: (*Great scorn*) War with the Turks! You fool! War with us, more likely! We're the ones who are going to catch it, not the Turks! This letter says that much!

Postmaster: Oh! That's different. Maybe it won't be war with the Turks.

Mayor: How do you feel about it, Iván Kóosmitch?

Postmaster: Me? Oh, I don't know. How do you feel?

Mayor: Well, I'm not frightened, but I am a little uneasy, about the trades-people. They say they've found me difficult, though God's my judge, if I have taken from one or two, I did it without any ill-feeling. (*Links arms with* **Postmaster** *and takes him aside*) I even think there may have been some secret denunciation of me. Why else should they send an Inspector here? Now listen, Iván Kóosmitch, this is for our mutual benefit. Couldn't you take every letter that passes through your post office, and, well, just unseal it a little bit, you know, and read it through. Then if there was no denunciation or anything, you could reseal it somehow, or send it on unsealed.

Postmaster: I know, I know . . . You're not teaching me anything. I've done it for years, not just as a precaution; I do like to know what goes on in the world. I tell you, it makes most interesting reading! And so edifying!

Mayor: Have you found anything about an official from Petersburg?

Postmaster: No! But plenty about those in Kostróma and Sarátov. It's a pity you did not read the letters. Wonderful tit-bits! The other day a lieutenant wrote to a friend, describing a ball in most sprightly language, very, very nicely. 'My life, dear friend, soars to Empyrean heights of pleasure,' he wrote, 'young women, music, hard riding.' He described it with deep feeling. I kept it on purpose. Would you like to read it?

Mayor: I can't be bothered now, but do me that favour, Iván Kóosmitch. If you find any complaint or denunciation, don't stop to think, keep it back.

Postmaster: I'll do that with pleasure.

Judge: I warn you, you'll get into trouble some day for that.

Mayor: Nonsense, nonsense. If you did anything publicly, mind, that would be different, but this is a family affair.

Activities

Short Stories

Background notes

Three of the stories in this section show the main characters as helpless victims of fate, they are also stories with a 'twist in the tail'. Thomas Hardy (1840–1928) wrote short stories, novels, and poems about his home county, Dorset, at a time when the outside world was changing the traditional way of life. Kate Chopin (1850–1904) lived in Louisiana and Missouri and, following the death of her husband brought up her six children on the money she received from publishing stories, poems, and essays. Chopin's interest in the relationship between the white plantation owners in Louisiana and their black slaves provides the background to several of her stories. Guy de Maupassant (1850–1893) worked as a clerk in Paris when his family fortune was lost during the French war with Germany in 1870. He became wealthy as a writer but was familiar with the life of the characters he describes in his story. Unlike the other stories in this section, Jane Austen's (1775–1817) comic tale presents love and marriage as a convenient arrangement which allowed young ladies to maintain a good standard of living. Austen describes a wealthy and leisurely world in her stories and novels but she herself never married and only had an allowance of £20 a year.

The Three Sisters

Note: this story is an ironic look at the novel written in letters, a popular form for novels in Austen's time.

Pair work

1   In the first letter, Mary is unsure whether to accept Mr Watts as a husband. Make two lists under these headings:

Reasons for accepting Mr Watts   Reasons for rejecting Mr Watts

2   What impression do you have of Mary from the first two letters? How does Austen create these impressions? Why does her mother call her *the strangest girl in the world?* What are her feelings about Mr Watts, her mother, and her sisters? What plan does she make to overcome her difficulties?

3   What do we learn about Mr Watts in the third letter? Why does Sophy laugh about Georgiana's description of him?

4   Letter 3 describes the conversation between Mary and Mr Watts in which they argue about the terms and conditions of their marriage. Record the argument under these headings:

What does Mary want?   What does Mary get?

5   Why do you think Austen chose to write her story as a series of letters? In what way would it have been different as a third-person narrative?

Group work

1   This is a comic story with serious messages about love and marriage. Discuss:

☐   What you find comic
☐   The messages that Austen conveys to the reader about love and marriage

2   *He seemed fatigued and disgusted . . . ridiculous conversation* and *Kitty made us all*

smile except Mary. Referring to these quotations, role play a scene between Mr Brudenell and Kitty in which they discuss the three Stanhope sisters after they have left Stoneham.

3   Role play a scene between Georgiana and Mary a year after Mary is married in which she tells her sister about married life with Mr Watts.

4   What features of the story tell you that it was written in the past? You should consider the language and spellings, characters' attitudes, and social details.

5   Prepare and present an account of life in the early 1800s amongst wealthy English families. You should include information on:

□   Domestic life
□   Sources of wealth
□   How women occupied their time
□   Fashions
□   Transport

You may choose to research each area independently or collaboratively.

Written assignment

Mary has her heart set on a new carriage, two footmen, a greenhouse, and a theatre in her home. She wants to spend part of her year in London and Bath and, like Sophy, to have a husband who will *consult my happiness in all his actions.*

Make a similar list for a young woman of the present day, including:

□   things she would want
□   places she would want to go
□   the type of relationship she would want with her partner

Write a short guide setting out what you think are the important elements in a good relationship. How have things changed since Austen's time?

The Necklace

Pair work

1   Maupassant creates a contrast between wealth and poverty in the first part of the story. Make a chart like this one showing the images which you think make this contrast clear. What is the importance of the contrast in the story as a whole?

Images of wealth	Images of poverty

2   What makes the young woman . . . *unhappy all the time?* (p. 11) What do you learn about her in this opening section of the story?

3   Look at the section from *One evening her husband . . . came home looking highly pleased with himself* (p. 12). What impression do you have of Mathilde's husband's character at this point and elsewhere in the story?

4   Look at the narrator's matter-of-fact way of describing the action at the most emotional moments: *They looked at each other . . . Finally Loisel got dressed again . . . He went out . . . She remained as she was* (p. 15). What does this tell you about his attitude towards the characters?

5   How do Mathilde and her husband solve the problem of the lost necklace and how does their life change in the following ten years?
6   What is ironic (p. 17) about the ending of the story?

Group work

1   *Life is so strange, so fickle. How little is needed to make or break us* (p. 17). Maupassant seems to blame fate for the Loisels' downfall. Another way of looking at the story is to say that Mathilde is to blame:
. . . *she felt that she was intended for a life of refinement and luxury*
She would have given anything to be popular, envied, attractive, and in demand
Discuss what and who is to blame for the Loisels' problems?
2   Mathilde and her husband face a moral dilemma when the necklace is lost. Discuss the two alternative solutions to this dilemma and decide which is most favourable.
☐   Replace necklace and work off debt
☐   Tell the owner and ask to be let off

Written assignment

1   Write another episode to follow Mathilde's meeting with her friend in which she returns home and tells her husband the truth about the necklace. How might it affect their relationship and their future plans?
2   Write a story in which the main character loses something precious belonging to someone else. You should include the characters' thoughts and show how they solve their problem.
    Write your story with the same detached tone as Maupassant. Read the following examples of Maupassant's tone in which he seems to be amused by their misfortune:
She was one of those pretty delightful girls who, apparently by some error of fate, get themselves born the daughters of very minor civil servants. (p. 11)

The Melancholy Hussar of the German Legion

Pair work

1   Reread from *Here stretch the downs . . . unexpectedly asked in marriage* (pp. 18–19). In this section Hardy concentrates on 'placing' his story in the remote past and a remote place. How does he make us aware of these two things and what effect do the time and place have on the mood in the story?
2   Next read on from *The king . . . aforesaid York Hussars* (pp. 19–21). Make a spider diagram putting in as much information as you can about the life and personalities of Phyllis, Dr Grove, and Humphrey Gould. Add to this chart as you read the story.
3   Now read from *The present generation . . . across this boundary* (part II). The presence of the soldiers is described as a . . . *golden radiance.*
☐   What impressions do you have of the soldiers so far?
☐   In what way does Matthäus Tina contradict this image?
4   Read on from *But news reached the village . . . confidence in him* (part III). What is Matthäus' plan? Why does Phyllis go along with it?
5   Continue to read from *It was on a soft . . . the door awaiting him* (part IV). What happens as Phyllis waits for Matthäus on the highway?
6   Finally, read from *Phyllis thanked him . . . Phyllis lies near* (part V). What unexpected news does Gould bring? How does Phyllis react to it?

- ☐ Pleased that she is free
- ☐ Bitter at having given up Matthäus
- ☐ Looking forward to being reunited with Matthäus
- ☐ Worried about whether Matthäus' plan was successful

Group work

1 The story is structured around unexpected events, such as the return of Gould and the execution of Matthäus. Each of the following events is a turning point in the story. Put the events into the correct sequence and then decide which of them contradict what is expected in some way.
- ☐ Phyllis witnesses Matthäus and Christophe's execution
- ☐ Dr Grove threatens to send Phyllis to her aunt's house
- ☐ Matthäus tells Phyllis his plan of escape
- ☐ Gould confesses that he is married
- ☐ Phyllis overhears Gould and another man talking about her
- ☐ Matthäus tells Phyllis about his mother's letters
- ☐ Gould gives Phyllis a silver mirror
- ☐ Phyllis tells Matthäus that she is not going to escape with him

2 This story is a love triangle in which Phyllis has to choose between two types of men. Continue this chart gathering information and commenting on the two characters

Gould	Matthäus
'...among these idlers' – not serious, only interested in gossip	'...a fine, tall soldier' – represents glamour, adventure

Why does Phyllis choose Gould in the end? Does she make the right choice?

Written assignments

1 Think carefully about the evidence from the story and decide what attitude the village gossips might have to Phyllis and Matthäus' relationship. Remember that the story is set in a small community, suspicious of outsiders. Script a conversation between two villagers in which they discuss the affair. These moments from the narrative may help you:

. . . you have been seen walking with him,
The older villagers . . . who know the episode from their parents,
. . . fragments of her story . . . which are most unfavourable to her character,
. . . not a native of the village,
. . . foreign barbarians, not much better than the French themselves

2 Imagine that you are Phyllis. Write a letter to Matthäus' mother telling her about the events which led up to her son's execution.

Désirée's Baby

Note: this story is set in Louisiana which, before American independence had been a French colony. Like other southern states, Louisiana's plantations were run with slave labour until the end of the American Civil War in 1865 when slavery was abolished.

Read *Twelve Years a Slave* (see pp. 73–77) before you read this story and find out as much as you can about slavery in the United States.

Pair work

1 Write a brief fact file for each of the characters introduced in the early part of the story.
2 What impressions do you have of L'Abri?
☐ How does Chopin create these impressions? Look closely at the imagery used.
☐ In what way does L'Abri reflect Aubigny's character?
3 What effect does marriage and fatherhood have on Aubigny and why does this please Désirée so much?
4 What happens when the baby is about three months old? What does Désirée become aware of and how does this affect her? How does this relate to Désirée becoming *miserable enough to die*?
5 What is ironic about the ending of the story (see p. 37)?

Group work

1 Read the scene between Désirée and Aubigny from *Presently her husband entered the room . . .* (p. 35) which ends *That was his last blow at fate* (p. 36). List all the words of physical movement. What do these words tell you about the feelings of the characters at this point? 'Hot seat' both characters and ask them to describe their thoughts and feelings during this scene.
2 Imagine that Désirée's disappearance is being treated as suspicious by the authorities. Interview these characters as part of police enquiries: Valmonde, Madame Valmonde, Aubigny, Zandrine.
3 Chopin's narrative method is to hint at what is happening rather than telling the reader directly. For example:

Hint	Actual event
' "Ah!" It was a cry she could not help'	Désirée finally accepts the truth

List any other hints in the same way.

Written assignments

1 Imagine that Désirée has written a suicide note before she goes down to the bayou. Write the note including her thoughts and feelings on:
☐ her life with Aubigny
☐ her childhood at Valmonde
☐ why she does not accept Madame Valmonde's invitation to return to Valmonde
☐ her thoughts on the treatment of the slaves
2 Désirée and her baby are innocent victims of racial prejudice. Write a story set in the present day in which the main character is destroyed by a similar prejudice.

Letters

Background notes

Before the telephone, the fax machine and e-mail, letters were the only alternative to talking directly with someone. All the letters in this section are private communications and reveal the writers' thoughts and feelings as well as the attitudes of the times. There has always been interest in the letters written by famous people, and they are often collected and published after the death of the writer. Some people have destroyed all their letters to avoid this happening: Alexander Pope was so worried about his public image that he asked for all his letters back and rewrote them before he died. Two of the letters in this section deal with 'public events' and the other three with the private lives of the writers. Chief Seattle's letter to the President of the United States seems to have been written for a wider audience. Sam's letter to his father records an eye-witness account of an historic event by an ordinary sailor. The other three letters deal with domestic events: the death of Charles Dickens' pet raven, Jane Austen's visit to Bath, and Percy Bysshe Shelley's letter of complaint to his friend's father.

To Cassandra (May 1801) *Jane Austen*

Note: in this letter Jane Austen writes to her sister, Cassandra. She has travelled to Bath from her country home near Winchester to stay with her aunt and uncle who are looking for a house to rent. Bath was a fashionable Spa town where wealthy people would spend part of their year passing their time by going to balls, visiting each other, and taking the waters.

Pair work

1 What has made her journey to Bath so pleasant? What does this tell you about travelling in Austen's time?
2 What evidence is there that Austen was fashion-conscious?

Group work

1 Discuss each of these statements, supporting your opinions with detailed evidence from the letter.
◻ Austen was a country girl unused to fashionable city life.
◻ Austen was from a rich family.
◻ Austen's family was not wealthy.
◻ Austen did not care about social status.
Support your opinions with evidence from the letter.
Present the results of your discussion in a chart.

Written assignment

Write a commentary on Austen's personality and attitudes as they are revealed in this letter. You should refer to the following parts of the letter:
◻ para 4, the chaise
◻ para 6, sleeping
◻ para 9, Mrs Chamberlayne
◻ para 12, prices in Bath
◻ para 13, the house in Green Park Buildings.

To his father (October or November 1805) *Sam*

Note: Sam was a sailor on the *Royal Sovereign* during the Battle of Trafalgar in 1805.

Pair work

1   What do you learn about Sam from this letter? Think about his personality as well as his attitudes.
2   Sam writes about the death of Lord Nelson in his letter. How has this affected the other sailors and the Admiral? What surprises Sam about their reaction?

Group work

1   In what way do the slang, jargon, and dialect words affect the tone of the letter? List these words and complete a chart like this one:

Slang/jargon/dialect	Standard English	Modern slang
rarely	thoroughly	good and proper

2   Prepare and present a radio news report of the Battle of Trafalgar in which you give an account of the battle. Allocate roles to each person so that you can include interviews with some of those who took part.

Written assignment

Sam is writing his letter somewhere off the Spanish coast. He thinks about home twice in the letter: *at Warnborough with my plough again* and *at Murrell Green Fair*.

Imagine that you are away from home and missing your family and familiar places. What thoughts of home come to you to cheer you up? Write a letter home in which you describe where you are and what you are doing. Include references to your 'home comforts'.

To Thomas Hitchener (14 May 1812) *Percy Bysshe Shelley*

Note: this letter was written by the poet, Percy Bysshe Shelley, to his friend's father, Thomas Hitchener who was a retired smuggler and publican. Mr Hitchener did not approve of the relationship between his daughter, Elizabeth, and Shelley.

Pair work

1   Mr Hitchener has clearly called Shelley's character into question in his last letter. How does Shelley turn Hitchener's argument on its head in the first paragraph?
2   Shelley is angry with Mr Hitchener because he will not allow Shelley to see Elizabeth. What has Mr Hitchener done that particularly annoys Shelley? What is Shelley complaining about in his questions?
3   Shelley is critical of Mr Hitchener in several ways. What are they?

Group work

In this letter the young Shelley is attacking the control of parents over children. Discuss his statement at the end of the letter.

Neither the laws of Nature, nor of England have made children private property.

- □ Do you agree with the statement? Be prepared to give your reasons.
- □ At what age do parents stop having rights over children? You should consider legal ages for specific activities, as well as more general rules about a child's:
- □ fashion and hair style
- □ TV watching
- □ coming-in times
- □ choice of friends, boy- or girl- friends

Written assignment

There are hints in this letter about the personalities of the three people involved:

Mr Hitchener's concern for his own *comfort* might mean that his wife is dead and he needs his daughter to look after him.

Shelley is upset and angry in this letter and this suggests that he was a hot-tempered young man with strong ideas about how people should behave. These characteristics are also seen in his *Sonnet: England in 1819* (see page 60).

Elizabeth is more of a mystery. She is either under her father's thumb and has let him write her reply to Shelley's invitation or she knows nothing about it and is wondering why she has not heard from Shelley. Remember that Shelley accuses Mr Hitchener of making her *very ill*.

Use your imagination to tell the story of these three people in this series of letters

- □ Hitchener's initial letter to Shelley (that prompts the response)
- □ Elizabeth's letter from her sick bed
- □ Shelley's reply to her

To Daniel Maclise (12 March 1841) *Charles Dickens*

Note: Charles Dickens and his family kept a pair of ravens at their house in London. This letter was written by Dickens just after the death of one of these ravens.

Pair work

1 Reread the letter carefully and then make a timetable for the main events leading to the death of the raven.

2 The raven is presented as a sick, elderly person. List the ways in which Dickens compares the bird to a human being.

3 What specific details do you find amusing in this letter?

Group work

Dickens writes about the raven as if he is describing the death of an elderly friend. This comparison is ironic because the death of a human is a more serious than the death of a bird. The tone of the letter appears to be serious until we read: *Under the influence of this medicine, he recovered so far as to be able at 8 o'Clock p.m. to bite Topping.* Find other examples of this ironic tone in the letter and explain the irony in each case.

Written assignment

The subject in Dickens' letter is a raven and its ironic comparison is with an elderly, sick man. Write about an event using an ironic tone. Choose one of the following situations.

Subject	Ironic comparison
Killing a wasp Cleaning the kitchen Children leaving school at the end of the day	Mortal combat between two enemies A ballet dancer A horse race

To the President of the United States (1854) *Chief Seattle*

Note: in 1855, the native American, Chief Seattle, gave his tribal lands to the United States in return for a reservation where they were allowed to live in peace. He did not want the reservation to be named after him fearing that, as a result, his spirit would be disturbed when he died.

Pair work

1 In the early part of this letter, why does Chief Seattle think that it is impossible to buy his tribal lands?
2 In what way are the beliefs of the native Americans described as different from white men's? Look specifically at the section from *We know that the white man . . . only a desert* (pp. 45–46) and the last four paragraphs of the letter.
3 In the latter parts of the letter Chief Seattle repeats that he is a *savage* and that *he does not understand*. In what way is he being ironic? What point is he making about the way the white men treat his environment? Do you agree with him?

Group work

1 At the end of the letter Chief Seattle writes *The end of living and the beginning of survival*. What does he mean? Reread these sentences from page 47:
   Whatever befalls . . . spit on themselves
   . . . the earth does not belong . . . man belongs to the earth
   Contaminate your bed . . . suffocate in your own waste
   Discuss each of these statements.
   What evidence is there in modern times that Chief Seattle was right in what he said? You might consider traffic pollution, oil-tanker 'spills' and holes in the ozone layer.
   What benefits are there from 'spoiling' the environment?
   Devise a ten-minute presentation in which you show the importance of protecting the environment. You might include quotations from Chief Seattle's speech in your presentation.
2 Prepare and present an account of the way the North American Indians were treated by the US army and government of the 1840s and 1850s.

Written assignment

Write a letter to the Prime Minister in which you state your concern about the environment in modern-day Britain. In your letter you should:
- □ point out who you hold responsible for damage caused to the environment
- □ suggest ways of preventing more damage being done

Poetry

Background notes

The poems in this section deal with particular themes. Time was an important subject when William Shakespeare (1564–1616) and Robert Herrick (1591–1674) were writing because life expectancy was short due to poor diet and a lack of medicines. The desire to overcome the passage of time is heard in their poems, in contrast to the Victorian poets Shelley (1792–1822) and A. E. Housman (1859–1936) who write about the insignificance of man's life. Jealousy, possessiveness, and frustration in love are heard in Thomas Carew (1595–1639) and Ben Jonson's (1572–1637) poems as well as the sadness of lost love in Christina Rossetti (1830–1894) and Moira O'Neill's (1864–1955) poems. The poems in Protest and The City were all written in the century when many people in Britain had moved from rural areas to work in the new industrial cities and the gap between the rich and the poor was very wide. Charles Lamb (1775–1834) and William Blake (1757–1827) write about the effect of urban living on ordinary people. The city is presented as glamorous in other sections of this book but here George Eliot (1819–1880) and Margaret Veley (1843–1887) show urban life as . . . *one huge prison*. Senses includes poems which celebrate the pleasures of taste, touch, sound, and sight in vivid imagery.

Understanding the poems

These exercises can be worked through for each unit in this section to build up a general understanding of the poems before attempting detailed questions.
1 Before you read the poems jot down what each title in the unit suggests to you. Discuss how reading the poems confirmed or changed your impressions of the titles.
2 Read the poems twice and make a note of:
- □ lines you liked
- □ any questions you have about the poems
- □ any words or lines you did not understand.
3 Fill in a chart like this:

Who is addressed?	What happens?	Where does the poem take place?	Who else is in the poem?

4 Identify any words or groups of words which tell you that the poems were not written in this century. These might include old-fashioned words (doth, twould) or examples of unusual word order. Look also for any objects or ideas which are no longer current in our society.

Time

Pair work

'Like as the waves make towards the pibled shore'

1   In the first line Shakespeare compares time to waves. What else is time compared to in the poem?
2   In the last line time is described as a *cruell hand*. In what way is time *cruell* and how does Shakespeare hope to overcome time?

To Dianeme

1   How does Herrick make us aware of the girl's beauty?
2   There is a *love-sick air* around the girl in the poem. What does this tell you about the kind of girl Dianeme is and the way she treats her suitors?

Ozymandias

1   Who are the four people in this poem? What attitude does the sculptor have to Ozymandias?
2   How has time changed Ozymandias' original purpose for having the statue made?
3   List all the words which suggest destruction and decay. How do these words help your understanding of the poem?

On Wenlock Edge

1   Housman uses the word *trouble* in the first and last verses. What is he referring to in both cases?
2   What mood does this poem give you? How do the central images of trees and wind contribute to this?
3   How does the image of the Roman soldier add to the theme of time in the poem? What comparison is made between the *Roman* and the *English yeoman*?

Group work

1   All of these poems use metaphors to express feelings and ideas more clearly. Find as many metaphors as you can and complete a chart like this:

Image	Metaphor	Effect
'those two eyes'	'starlike sparkle in their skies'	Eyes made to sound bright, heavenly, dazzling

2   Shakespeare and Housman compare time to waves and wind, and people to pebbles and trees respectively. In what ways are these suitable comparisons? Which do you think is most effective and what attitude does each comparison reveal about time and people?

3   *'Like as the waves make towards the pibled shore'* and *To Dianeme* are addressed to women but present different purposes and attitudes. What purpose does each poet have in writing the poems? Support your ideas with quotations.

Written assignment

1   There are two attitudes to time in these poems:
'We're only here for a short time so we'd better make the best of it.'
'In a hundred years no one will remember us so our lives are insignificant.'
Look at the final lines of these poems and decide what attitude to time is shown by each one.
Write a commentary on the poems in which you contrast the language they use to convey their attitudes to time.
2   In *The Melancholy Hussar of the German Legion* (see pp. 18–32), Hardy sets his tale in the past. There is a strong sense that the characters and their troubles are all long gone. Write about Hardy's treatment of time and compare it to *On Wenlock Edge* and any other poems in this unit.

Love

Pair work

To Celia

1   The 'voice' in this poem is trying to persuade Celia to sleep with him. List his arguments putting them in your own words.
2   What are the problems involved in the relationship the 'voice' is proposing? Who is being referred to in the line *his easier ears beguile*? What does this tell you about the ages of those involved?
3   What tone of voice should be used when reading this poem?

The Spring

1   What contrast does Carew create in the first twelve lines?
The subject is a woman's rejection of him – why do you think he wrote this long introduction about nature?
2   How does the woman not . . . *keepe/Time with the season*? What seasons are her feelings compared to?

The Bracelet: To Julia

1   Why does the 'voice' in the poem tie a *silken twist* around Julia's wrist? What is hinted at about their relationship in the lines *But to showe there how, in part,/Thou my pretty captive art*.
2   What makes it easier for Julia to escape and more difficult for the 'voice' to do so?

'Youth gone and beauty gone if ever there'

1   What do the second and the fifth lines tell you about the 'voice's' view of herself?
2   What is the mood of the poem?
3   Why will she only seek *common flowers as blow with corn*? What do roses and *common flowers* represent for her?

Sea Wrack

1   How does the strong rhythmic beat reflect the actions in this poem?
2   What is implied about the relationship between the man and the woman in the fourth line?
3   What is the importance of the sea wrack in their relationship?
4   What else . . . *may drift ashore* apart from the sea wrack?

Group work

1   The women addressed in *To Celia* and *The Spring* resist the advances of their lovers. How and why do the moods in the poems differ?
2   There is a mystery in '*Youth gone . . .* ' It appears to be about Rossetti regretting her loss of youth and beauty, but look at the final five lines. Discuss what you think has happened to her.
3   *To Celia* is a poem of persuasion. One person in the group should think of a treasured object. The others should then try to persuade them to give it up.
4   The first three poems were written in the Sixteenth and Seventeenth Centuries, the others in the Nineteenth. What can you find in common in these two groups? Look closely at the tone, language, and attitudes of the poems.

Written assignments

1   Write a reply to someone who thinks that *Youth gone and beauty gone, what doth remain?* This could be in prose or poetry.
2   Three of these poems are addressed to someone in particular. Think carefully about the personalities, attitudes, and situations in each poem. Choose one and write a letter in reply from the person addressed.
3   Two of these poems deal with lost love. Write a comparison of the treatment of this theme in *Sea Wrack*, '*Youth gone and beauty gone if ever there*', and *Désirée's Baby* (see pp. 33–37).

Protest

Pair work

A Ballad

1   Complete a chart like this to show the main contrast in the poem:

Wealth/comfort	Poverty/hardship

How is this contrast reflected in the way each verse is organized?
2   How effective is the poem at making you feel sorry for the poor?

Holy Thursday

Note: Holy Thursday is the old name for Ascension Day on which Christ rose to heaven after His crucifixion.

1 In verse 1, how does Blake criticize the . . . *rich and fruitful land?*
2 What is ironic about the title of the poem?

Sonnet: England in 1819

1 What impression do you have of England in 1819 from this poem?
2 In the first line Shelley criticizes the king, George III. What other groups of people is he critical of and why?
3 What effect do you think Shelley was trying to achieve by his lists of faults in the poem? What clue does the last line hold?

The Latest Decalogue

Note: this poem is a rewriting of some of the Ten Commandments in The Bible. (From Hebrew: *deka logoi* – ten commandments.)

1 Why do you think Clough wrote this poem in the form of rhyming couplets?
2 Each commandment given is followed by a reason for obeying it. Complete a chart like this, giving the original purpose of the commandment.

Commandment	Original reason	Reason in the poem
Thou shalt not steal	Respecting other's property	Cheating is more profitable

Group work

1 List the Ten Commandments from The Bible. Discuss them and agree on an order of importance for living in today's world. Which commandments do you think are out of date? Write your own list of commandments as a recipe for a 'happy' life.

2 The mood in *Sonnet: England in 1819* is openly angry in contrast to *The Latest Decalogue*. In *Holy Thursday*, Blake uses the techniques of the political speech writer, such as rhetorical questions. Decide what the mood is of each of these poems, making a note of any changes of mood within each. Perform the poems bringing out these contrasting moods.

3 *A Ballad, Holy Thursday* and *Sonnet: England in 1819* were all written in the Nineteenth Century in protest at the social conditions suffered by the poor. Each choose one of the following headings and research this aspect of the social history of the period:

☐ Education
☐ Living Conditions
☐ Working Conditions
☐ The Family

Using your research, prepare and give a presentation.

Written assignments

1 These poets use their poetry to attack the corruption they see in their society. They are protest poems against those in power who are making the poor and vulnerable suffer. If they were writing today what targets do you think they might attack? Present your conclusions as a speech or a letter of protest, designed to get the message across most effectively.

2 A sonnet is a poem, of fourteen lines, usually written in rhyming couplets and sometimes containing the 'punch line' in the final couplet of the poem. Look through the poetry units and identify the sonnets. Write a comparison of them considering:
□ Form and rhyme
□ Imagery and metaphor
□ Mood and tone
□ Purpose and most effective use of sonnet form

3 The gap between the rich and the poor, those with power and the powerless, is addressed in this unit. The extract from *The Government Inspector* (see pp. 96–100) has the same theme but presents it in a comic way. Write a comparison of these two approaches, saying which you find most effective.

The City

Pair work

In a London Drawing Room

1 What impression do you get of the city from the first line? What other images from the poem add to this?

2 *Monotony of surface and of form/Without a break to hang a guess upon.* What is Eliot suggesting here about the freedom of being able to guess?

3 How does Eliot portray the city dwellers' state of mind?

A Town Garden

1 The main contrast in the poem is between the city and the country. Complete a chart like this to show how the imagery of the garden conveys this contrast.

City	Country
'a brick built trap'	'washed with rain and hung with pearls'

2 Reread the final verse. Why does Veley say the rose serves a better purpose in the city?

3 The final two lines refer to Socrates the Greek philosopher who committed suicide by drinking hemlock and to Christ who was crucified on the ... *cross of pain.* How do these images relate to the rest of the poem?

London

1 Blake presents London as a nightmare place where the *Infant's cry of fear* is heard. What other images of fear and horror are in the poem?
2 In the final line Blake connects marriages with funerals. What does this tell you about the mood of the poem as a whole?

Ballade of a Special Edition

Note: a special edition is a newspaper produced after an important or sensational event.
1 What event has caused this special edition? What other news events are mentioned in the poem?
2 Who is the . . . *herald and the friend* and what is he doing?
3 Why does Levy accuse the newspaper of being a cheat and what is hinted at in the line *Imagination's aid is tried*? What is the effect of repeating the last line?

Group work

1 Think about when you were last in a big city. What aspects of city life in the poems are the same and which are different today? The poets paint a dark picture of city life. Can you see why?
2 Do you agree with Levy's criticism of newspapers? Which of these two statements do you think motivates the press?

'The public has a right to know about violent and disturbing stories.'	'We print violent stories because they improve sales.'

Written assignments

1 Using lines from the poem and pictures make a collage of nineteenth-century London as it is presented in the poems.
2 Write a reply to the poems' view of the city in which you present a brighter picture.
3 *In a London Drawing Room* and *A Town Garden* show how nature is spoilt by the city. Veley uses the image of the rose to represent the effect on ordinary people of city life. Write a critical account bringing out this contrast and referring to the people in the poems as a whole.
4 In her letter *To Cassandra* (see p. 38), Jane Austen tells of her visit to Bath. Write about the ways in which Austen's experience of the town contrasts with the poems in this unit.

Senses

Pair work

Plum Blossom

Note: this is an early twelfth-century Chinese poem in a modern translation.
1 Who are the people in the poem and what do you learn about them?
2 Although there is no rhyme pattern in the poem there is a clear rhythm. How is this achieved?
3 Many of the words in the poem have long vowel sounds: *slanting, puzzling, frowning*. How do these sounds help to create the mood of the poem?

Belinda's Toilet

Note: this is part of a longer poem called *The Rape of the Lock* in which Belinda has a lock of hair cut off by an admirer. In this passage Belinda is doing her toilet which means putting on her jewellery and her make-up.

1   Belinda's toilet is compared to a religious ceremony. What does this tell you about Belinda's view of herself? How do the images used appeal to the senses?

2   What is ironic about Pope's attitude to Belinda?

3   What tells you that this poem was written in the past? Look closely at the language and content of the extract.

Market Women's Cries

1   How do the women try to persuade people to buy their produce? Complete a chart like this to identify their different sales methods.

Produce	Cooking tips	Medical benefits	Other reasons
Apples			To maintain her family

2   Which words give you an impression of real speech and an everyday situation? How does the use of the first person give the poem more impact?

3   Does this rhythm add to or spoil the realistic mood of the poem?

Group Work

1   Each of these poems relies on its effect by appealing to our senses. Discuss what you think are the most memorable and effective images and group them under these headings.
☐ Sight
☐ Sound
☐ Smell
☐ Touch

2   Rehearse and perform your favourite poem.

3   *Belinda's Toilet* describes a fashionable young lady putting on her make-up. It comes from a poem written in 1714. Present an account of what clothes and other adornments were fashionable amongst the wealthy at that time.

Written assignment

1   Write an account of a lively scene using imagery of the senses. For instance:
☐ a city street
☐ a fairground
☐ a school fete
You could group your impressions of different aspects of the scene under headings as Swift does.

2   In Edith Wharton's *In Morocco* (see pp. 78–81), she concentrates on the sensual delights of the Bahia and the Souk. Using *Plum Blossom* as a model, select images from *In Morocco* and arrange them into two poems one called 'The Bahia', the other 'The Souk'.

Reportage

Background notes

Reportage can be defined as an account of people, events, and places witnessed at first-hand by the writer. When events are told by the people who were there at the time they are brought to life and even ordinary experience can be made surprising and unique. The Frenchman, Hippolyte Taine (1823–1892) spent ten weeks in England in 1871, travelling around the country. In his *Notes on England*, he records his impressions. In his foreigner's view of England, it is possible to detect tones of approval and disapproval as he comments on the London docks. Taine describes the people he comes across there in this passage as *slaves*. Their living conditions are similar to the black American slaves in *Twelve Years a Slave* by Northup. Published in the Nineteenth Century, Solomon Northup gives an account of life on cotton plantations in the southern states of America which exposes the horrors of slavery. He describes his experiences factually but occasionally it is possible to hear in his writing the deep anger he felt at his situation. In contrast to these texts, the American writer and novelist Edith Wharton's (1861–1937) descriptions of Morocco concentrate on the exotic sights, sounds and smells of her stay. Wharton came from a wealthy New York family and spent much of her married life living in Europe. It was while she was living in France that she visited Morocco. It was a chance to spend time on her own away from an unhappy marriage and a husband who was becoming mentally ill.

Notes on England

Pair work

1 Taine is both impressed and disgusted by the London docks. Read the extract carefully and make a note of the features of the docks which have made an impression on the writer. You will need to note features of which he approves as well as disapproves.
2 Taine was a Frenchman travelling in England. What evidence is there that this piece was written by a foreigner?

Group work

1 Taine ends this piece by describing the poverty he has seen as . . . *the real sore on the body of English society*. Read the Protest poems (see pp. 57–61). Discuss the similarities between these poems and Taine's description. Which do you find most effective as a criticism of society? Discuss what you consider to be the 'sores' of present day life in Britain.
2 Research the modern-day London docklands. Present the contrast between nineteenth-century and present-day docklands in one of the following forms: a playscript, a collage, a documentary, or a role play.

Written assignments

1 Using the last three paragraphs from the extract, rearrange some of its phrases into a poem. Write a commentary on why you chose particular phrases and why they make a good poem.
2 Taking the locations and setting in this extract, write a story in which the central character is one of the *dirty, barefoot* children.

Twelve Years a Slave

Pair work

1 Write a fact file on 'cotton' basing your information on this extract.

2 What impression do you have of the life of a slave from this extract? Gather evidence from the extract under these headings:

□ Living conditions

□ Work

□ Treatment by white people

□ Food

What attitude to black people do these extracts reveal?

Written assignment

Imagine that you are to make an anti-slavery speech in the American House of Representatives at the time when slavery was still imposed. Using the information from this narrative and any other research (see *Désirée's Baby*, pp. 33–37), write and deliver the speech in which you try to persuade your audience that slavery should be abolished. Reading some examples of fine speech-writing before you attempt this assignment, for example speeches by Martin Luther King and Winston Churchill, will be helpful.

In Morocco

Pair work

1 What does Wharton enjoy about her stay in Marrakech?

2 Apart from the swallows, what visitors does Wharton have?

Group work

Discuss the attractions of Marrakech as a tourist destination as presented by Wharton. Select details from the text and devise a two-minute broadcast for a radio travel programme. Include parts for a presenter, some holiday-makers, and a representative of the Moroccan tourist board. Tape record your broadcast.

Written assignment

In this extract, Wharton describes two contrasting settings – the Bahia and the bazaar. Look closely at the language and imagery Wharton uses to describe both places and decide what contrasting moods she manages to convey. Write a commentary based on your conclusions, including evidence from the text.

Drama

Background notes

Lucian (AD 115–200) was a lawyer by profession who held an important position on the staff of the Governor of Egypt. His plays and 'sketches' make fun of religion, philosophy, and those in positions of power. His 'satirical' treatment of serious subjects made him very unpopular during his lifetime. Like the extract from Lucian's play, *She Stoops to Conquer* takes a comical look at human vanity. Oliver Goldsmith (1730–1774) was born in Ireland but spent most of his life abroad, firstly as a failed medical student in Edinburgh and eventually as a playwright in London. Despite his success as a writer, Goldsmith was usually in debt and died, poisoning himself by mistake with his own medicines, leaving £2000 of unpaid bills. Many of Shakespeare's (1564–1616) plays deal with kingship, power, and ambition. *Macbeth* was performed in front of King James, who ruled England and Scotland, and the play is a compliment to James' kingship as it shows how his ancestors brought order and peace to Scotland after the defeat of Macbeth. In the scene from *Macbeth* Macbeth and Lady Macbeth try to hide the truth and this theme is also evident in the scene from Gogol's (1809–1852) play, *The Government Inspector*. Gogol lived in St Petersburg but left Russia in 1836 when he was sacked from his university job. He spent the rest of his life abroad, living for a long time in Rome. Gogol's plays attack those in positions of power by exposing the corruption and hypocrisy of a group of petty officials in a small provincial town.

No Baggage Allowance

Note: in Greek Mythology Charon and Hermes are associated with the journey into the afterlife. Charon was the miserly ferryman who would collect the money left with the dead by their relatives. If no money was left, the souls of the dead would be left on the banks of the River Styx. Hermes was the god who conducted the dead from the mortal world to the Underworld.

Pair work

1   What two types of luggage are the characters 'carrying'? Why is it important for them to lose both types of luggage?
2   What impression do you have of each character as Hermes questions them? How is Menippus different to the others?
3   Prepare a performance of Charon's first two speeches. Decide what kind of character he is and what would be a suitable tone of voice for the performance.

Group work

1   Discuss what you find comic about *No Baggage Allowance*. What similarities are there between the comedy in this scene and Dickens' letter (see pp. 43–44)?
2   Lucian is using his writing to ridicule certain types of people in the society in which he lived. Put one group member into the 'hot seat' as Lucian, the writer. The rest of the group should question 'Lucian' to find out what he hoped to achieve in this scene and what comment he was making on society.

Written assignment

It's no good, we've all got to stand our trial... Write a script for the last judgement scene mentioned at the end of this piece. Include any information on the characters you can find in the scene. Each character will have to defend himself in an attempt to get into heaven and avoid going to hell.

Macbeth

Pair work

1   The audience knows that Macbeth has just murdered King Duncan. He and Lady Macbeth are hiding their guilt by pretending to be shocked by his death. What do they say and do to achieve this?
2   Look carefully at the language in this scene. What imagery is used to describe the dead king? What does this tell you about the status of kings at the time?
3   What is the significance of the conversation between Lennox and Macbeth before Macduff re-enters with the news of the king's murder?

Group work

1   Discuss your views on secrecy and deception. Are there any circumstances in which they are justified? Have you ever hidden the truth and, if so, what were the consequences?
2   Imagine that two people have stolen a wallet from one of the changing rooms at school. They have hidden the wallet in a secret place and will return to it later. Meanwhile, they are involved in a conversation between the owner of the wallet and a group of friends. Improvise the scene and call it 'The Cover Up'.

Written assignment

In this extract and *The Government Inspector* (see pp. 96–100) the characters are worried about being found out. Write a comparison of the two texts commenting on which you think is the most effective.

She Stoops to Conquer

Pair work

1   How does Hastings flatter Mrs Hardcastle and encourage her vanity?
2   What does the conversation with Tony add to your impression of Mrs Hardcastle's character?
3   How are country and city life contrasted in this extract?

Group work

1   What do you learn about fashionable life in London at the time this play was written? Discuss what might have been the advantages and disadvantages of such a life.
2   Make a note of any words or phrases that tell you this was written in the past. Using these words and phrases, perform a scene between Mrs Hardcastle and her husband in which she complains about him being a *piece of antiquity* and he refuses to go to London.
Compare your version with the opening of the play.

Written assignments

1 Script a conversation between Hastings and one of his fashionable friends in which he describes Mrs Hardcastle and says what he really thinks of her.

2 Although Mrs Hardcastle is a comic character she is also rather sad, only being able to *enjoy London at second-hand*. Imagine that you live a long way from a city and are longing for the 'buzz' of city life. Write a piece in which you convey your feelings.

The Government Inspector

Pair work

1 The characters in the scene are worried that their corrupt habits will be found out by the inspector. Make notes on the different ways in which all the characters are corrupt.

2 What part will the Postmaster play in hiding the truth from the inspector?

Group work

1 Imagine that the inspector has now arrived in the town and inspected the courtroom, hospital, and school house. Role play the conversations he has with: the Mayor, the Judge, the Charity Commissioner, and the School Superintendent.

2 This is a humorous scene with a serious purpose in which those in positions of power are ridiculed so as to expose their corrupt ways. This type of humour is called satire. Read *No Baggage Allowance* (pp. 82–87), *She Stoops To Conquer* (pp. 92–95), and *Belinda's Toilet* (p. 67). What is the point of the satire in each of these pieces?

Written assignment

This scene, *No Baggage Allowance* (pp. 82–87), and the Protest poems (pp. 57–61) all attack corruption among the rich and powerful in society. Write a critical commentary in which you compare these pieces. Comment particularly on: language and tone, characterization, which is the most effective attack, and the writers' intentions.

Extended Activities

1 Read *Twelve Years a Slave* and *Désirée's Baby* before attempting this assignment. Zandrine is the nurse-maid in *Désirée's Baby*. She is silent and obedient but the writer hints that she knows what is going on between the master and his wife. Script a scene between Zandrine and La Blanche (another slave) in which they talk about: Aubigny's treatment of them; the change in the master and mistress' relationship and the possible reason for it; the disappearance of Désirée; Aubigny's bonfire. You should use information from *Twelve Years a Slave* in the scene.

2 In her letter to her sister, *To Cassandra*, Jane Austen tells her that someone called Martha has had a triumph. This probably refers to her engagement to a wealthy man. Read Austen's story *The Three Sisters* in which Mary's 'triumph' is described. Write a story, using the letter form, entitled 'Martha's Triumph'.

3 Three of the short stories have 'twists in the tail'. Write a story with a surprise ending and which begins with this sentence from *The Necklace*:
Life is so strange, so fickle. How little is needed to break us.

4 Apart from the dates on the letters, what else tells you that they were written in the past? Write about one of the letters, considering the language, social details, events included, objects and equipment mentioned.

5 In *Belinda's Toilet*, the writer compares Belinda making up for the day to a religious ceremony. Dickens' letter *To Daniel Maclise* also compares his subject to something else. Write a comparison of these two texts, commenting on what you think the authors' intentions are in both cases.

6 Several texts in this book are critical of human behaviour. Vanity and pride are exposed through humour in *The Three Sisters* and *She Stoops to Conquer*, in contrast to the serious and sinister scene from *Macbeth* which portrays murder and deception. Choosing three or four texts from any section in the book, write a commentary on what targets in human behaviour the authors were attacking. Refer closely to the texts and include your views on: which is the most effective, the way the characters are represented, the language used to convey the mood of the texts.

7 The tone or mood in this book varies from text to text. In *Sonnet: England in 1819* you can hear the anger in Shelley's lines: *A people starved and stabbed in the fields*. This can be contrasted to the peaceful mood of Wharton's descriptions of Morocco: *Along court . . . where pigeons plume . . . and the dripping tiles glitter with refracted sunlight*. Sam's letter to his father is cheery and chatty, referring to his lost fingers he says . . . *that's not much, it might have been my head.*

Write a commentary on these texts in which you compare the tone of the writing and say how this reflects the experience of the time described.

8 Nature and the countryside is usually presented in a positive way in the texts in this anthology (with the exception of *She Stoops to Conquer*). The city, on the other hand, is presented as dangerous, full of poverty, and unhealthy. Choose some of the following texts and write about the way each author portrays the country or the city. You should refer closely to the texts you choose.
The Melancholy Hussar of the German Legion; To Cassandra (May 1801); To the President of the United States (1854); The Spring; A Town Garden; London; Ballade of a Special Edition; Notes on England; She Stoops to Conquer.

9   Look closely at the language used in the following texts and write a commentary on any differences and changes in the English language that you have noticed.
Sixteenth/Seventeenth Centuries: *To Celia, The Spring, Macbeth*
Eighteenth Century: *The Three Sisters, Market Women's Cries, She Stoops to Conquer*
Nineteenth Century: *To Cassandra, To his Father, To Thomas Hitchener, Notes on England*

10   There are some memorable characters in this anthology. A writer portrays character by what they say, what others say about them, what they do, and what the author says about them. Choose three characters. Give your impressions of them and comment on how the authors present the characters.

11   Many of the texts in this anthology are more than 100 years old. The language and social references are often out-of-step with our own. One complaint about studying 'old texts' is that they are not relevant to today's world. Write a response to this criticism arguing that many of the experiences described are still familiar. For example, Carew complains of his love playing hard to get in *The Spring*. This is still a problem faced by lovers! The issue of the gap between rich and poor, described in Shelley's *Sonnet: England in 1819*, is also a big problem today.

12   Choosing any of the texts, write a letter to the author discussing the themes of their work. For instance, you might write to Solomon Northup and tell him that things have changed since his time but that there is still racial tension in many countries of the world; or you might tell Shakespeare that his writing had '*defeated time*' as it is still read and enjoyed today.

Wider Reading

Assignment 1 – Satire

Many of the texts in this book are critical of some aspect of human behaviour or society. Some of them present characters and events in a comical way in order to make them look and sound ridiculous. This technique, in which the comedy has a serious, critical purpose, is called satire. For instance, in *No Baggage Allowance* (see pp. 82–87) Lucian is humorous but also attacks human vanity and greed.

Choose a book from the list below and write about how successful you think the author has been at presenting character and theme. Make notes as you read on these aspects:

☐ Comic scenes and what they tell you about what the author is attacking through their satire. Do you agree with the author's point of view?

☐ What aspects of human behaviour do the main characters represent? Do the characters change or stay the same as the story develops? What contrasts are there between the characters and does this lead to conflicts in the plot?

☐ What is the setting? Does this contribute to the book as a whole? Does the setting affect the way the characters behave?

☐ Is the plot plausible or difficult to believe? If it is hard to believe how might this be part of the satire?

> *Pride and Prejudice*, Jane Austen
> *She Stoops to Conquer*, Oliver Goldsmith, ed E. Benn, New Mermaids, 1979
> *The Alchemist*, Ben Jonson, ed E. Benn, New Mermaids, 1966
> *Loot*, Joe Orton, Methuen, 1967
> *Riotous Assembly*, Tom Sharpe, Pan, 1996
> *Gulliver's Travels*, Jonathan Swift, Penguin, 1962
> *Catch 22*, Joseph Heller, Vintage, 1994
> *Slaughterhouse 5*, Kurt Vonnegut, Jonathan Cape, 1970
> *The Loved One*, Evelyn Waugh, Penguin, 1951
> *The Importance of Being Earnest*, Oscar Wilde, ed E. Benn, New Mermaids, 1980

Assignment 2 – The urban environment

Several texts in this book are concerned with the way cities influence the lives of those who live in them. The emphasis in this anthology is on London in the Nineteenth Century when poverty and hardship were commonplace.

1   Read one twentieth-century and one pre-twentieth-century book from the list on page 127. Make notes as you read on these aspects:

☐ How is the town or city represented in each book? What are your impressions of urban life from each book? Do you think these are realistic representations of life in the town/city?

☐ How does the town/city affect the lives of the characters? Is the wealth and social position of the characters important?

2   Read one novel and one non-fiction book.

☐ What purpose do you think each author had in writing their books?

☐ What differences do you notice in the way the urban environment is presented in each book?

Fiction

Mary Barton, Elizabeth Gaskell, Penguin 1970
The Big Sleep, Raymond Chandler, Penguin 1949
Hard Times, Charles Dickens, Penguin 1985
It's a Battlefield, Graham Greene, Penguin 1940
Brighton Rock, Graham Greene, Penguin 1943
Hangover Square, P. Hamilton, Penguin 1956
Washington Square, Henry James, Penguin 1963
Dubliners, James Joyce, Penguin 1956

Non-fiction

Neither Here Nor There, Bill Bryson, Minerva, 1993
Among the Cities, Jan Morris, Penguin, 1986
The Faber Book of London, ed. A. N. Wilson, Faber, 1993

Assignment 3 – Romance

Read two of the books listed below and write a comparison of them. Make notes as you read on the following aspects:

☐ Are there any similarities in the way the plots develop? At what points in the story are there problems for the central characters? How and when are these problems sorted out? Do the stories end happily or unhappily? Which ending do you prefer?

☐ What impressions do you have of the main characters? Do you think they are convincing?

☐ What do you think are the essential ingredients of a good love story? Give details of character, setting, plot, and point of view.

Emma, Jane Austen, Penguin, 1966
Fair Stood the Wind for France, H. E. Bates, Penguin, 1958
Jane Eyre, Charlotte Bronte, Penguin, 1966
The French Lieutenant's Woman, John Fowles, Jonathan Cape, 1969
Far From the Madding Crowd, Thomas Hardy, Macmillan, 1957
A Farewell to Arms, Ernest Hemingway, Penguin, 1935
Sons and Lovers, D. H. Lawrence, Penguin, 1948
The Ballad of the Sad Café, Carson McCullers, Penguin, 1963

Discover more fabulous
Nantucket novels by

Nancy
Thayer

Go to www.headline.co.uk to find out more

Kennedy flopped back against the pillows. 'By ME, you mean Alonzo. Sex.'

Katya rolled her eyes and directed the subject back to the holidays. 'So. You can order chocolates for Nicole online. Go Godiva, that's always easy and best. Send her the biggest box. They'll gift wrap it. *Done.* For your father, go online and order a few of the newest biographies. You know all the man does is read.' Katya yawned. 'SO boring.'

'Mommy.' Kennedy didn't like her parents criticizing each other.

'What did you get James?'

'Nothing yet.' Kennedy poked her enormous belly. 'Maybe I'll order him a life-size blow-up doll he can have sex with.'

Katya ignored this. 'Does he need a new golf bag? Tennis whites?'

'For Christmas? In New England? We can't go anywhere, may I remind you, because this baby boy is coming in January. So, no Florida, no Aruba, just snow.'

'Now let's be positive. How about cross-country skis for James and for Maddox? They can go out together.'

'That's a good idea. I've ordered a sled from L.L. Bean for Maddox.' Kennedy gazed around the living room. No tree, no pines on the fireplace mantel, no presents. 'What are you doing for Christmas?'

'I told you, Kennedy. Where is your mind these days? Alonzo and I are going to a cleansing spa in Switzerland for ten days. No fats, no alcohol, no sugar. Lots of exercise and fresh air. Indoor tennis, of course.'

'You told me you were going to a spa, but you didn't say Switzerland!' Kennedy sat up, alarmed. 'Mommy, what about the baby?'

'Kennedy, he's not due until the middle of January. I'll be back on December thirtieth. Plenty of time.'

'You've got to be!' Kennedy ran her hands over her belly. 'I need you there, and Daddy and James.'

'We'll do our best.'

'I know you will. Still—'

'Ssh. It's going to be fine.' Katya glanced at her watch. 'I've got my yoga class in about thirty minutes . . .'

'I know. I should get Maddox home for his dinner, anyway.' Kennedy pushed her arms back, trying to extract herself from the sofa.

Katya watched her daughter with an assessing eye. 'I promised to give you money for a nanny.'

'I know, Mommy, and I'm grateful. But I want to bond with the new baby, even if he is a boy.'

'It's a shame about that. Girls' clothes are so much cuter. But never mind, Kennedy, it will be fun for Maddox to have a brother to play with.'

Kennedy had achieved a standing position. 'I wish James would take a week's vacation and spend it with me and the new baby, and especially with Maddox. It would be wonderful for Maddox to have his father give him special attention when we have a new baby.'

'James has an important job with his brokerage firm, Kennedy. You're being far too idealistic with this bonding mumbo-jumbo. Get a nanny, let her care for the baby, and *you* spend time with Maddox. I had a nanny for you, and you turned out all right.'

Kennedy lumbered across the room and into the hall. She pressed the intercom and told Alonzo that he should bring Maddox up.

'Maddox wants a puppy,' she said over her shoulder to her mother. 'I told him no. I can't deal with a puppy and a new baby. Plus, I'm allergic to animals.'

'Are you, darling? I never knew that.'

Kennedy stared at her mother. 'I thought that was why we never had a pet.'

'Oh? I must have forgotten.' Katya opened the closet door and took out Maddox's little black dress coat and wool cap. She handed them to Kennedy. 'I'm sure you're right.'

Chapter Seven

It was the middle of December. Nicole wore a blue roll-neck cotton pullover with a large white snowflake in the center. She'd opened her holiday jewelry box and selected snowflake earrings to match. They'd cost less than five dollars and were iridescent – she could still remember how pleased she was to discover them at a local pharmacy. She looked pretty cute, even if she did say so herself. Kennedy, of course, would consider her sweater sappy. But Kennedy wasn't here yet.

And today they were going to buy the tree!

They bundled up in puffy down coats and leather gloves and drove out of town to Moors End Farm on Pol-pis Road.

Snow wasn't falling, but the wind blew fiercely, and overhead the sky hung low and white, as if ready to drop its load of flakes at any moment. Sebastian squeezed the car between two others. He and Nicole slammed their car doors and leaned into the wind, battling toward the trees propped against wooden supports.

Nicole headed toward the tallest trees. After a moment, she noticed Sebastian was no longer beside her. He'd stalked over to the area with the midget trees.

'Sebastian!' she called. 'Over here!'

Sebastian waved to her, indicating that she should come over to where he stood.

'No!' Nicole called. 'Tall!' She raised her arms high and wide. 'BIG!'

Sebastian hurried over to her, looking worried. 'Nicole, we don't have the decorations or the lights for such a large tree.'

Nicole wriggled cheekily. '*I* do. I brought a couple of boxes when I moved here. Plus, we can buy more lights in a flash!'

Sebastian chuckled at her weak joke. 'I'm afraid I'm not much help with all this tree business.'

'You'll be all the help I need when you carry it into the house,' Nicole assured him.

A burly sales clerk in a red-checked flannel jacket and a fuzzy green hat appeared.

'What about this one?' he suggested, pulling out an eight-foot-tall tree and shaking it so its branches fell away a bit from their tightly twined position.

'Look, Seb, it's *flawless*.' Nicole clapped her hands in delight. She'd never seen such a sublime evergreen. 'It's shaped like an A. Each side is bushy, so we won't have to tuck one bad side in a corner to hide it.'

Sebastian glanced fondly at his wife, who was practically levitating in her pleasure. 'Okay,' he surrendered. 'This tree.'

At the small shed where they paid, Nicole bought a wreath for the front door, too. A *tasteful* wreath with a large red bow and nothing else, no small decorations, no candy canes, no pine cones dusted with faux snow, which she would have preferred. This was her private concession to Sebastian's decorous (lackluster) tastes. While he and Katya had never had a Christmas tree in the house, Nicole couldn't imagine Christmas without one.

With the lumberjack's help, Sebastian easily hefted the tree to the top of his SUV and fastened it with rope and bungee cords.

Getting it into the house was a different matter entirely. The tree was heavy. Sebastian removed the cords and wrestled it to the ground, but once he'd gotten his hands on the trunk, he had trouble lifting it and for a moment stumbled around the car as if dancing with a clumsy drunk in a green fir coat.

Nicole stifled a giggle. 'Let me take the top to guide it in.' She stuck her hands in between the branches, grabbed the slender trunk, and together they carried it into the living room. They dropped it on the floor, then wrestled it into the stand Nicole had placed in readiness.

Sebastian stood back, staring at the tree. 'It's awfully big.'

'I know,' Nicole agreed smugly. She cocked her head, studying her husband. 'Tell you what. If you'll help me put the lights on, I'll do the rest of the decorating.'

His posture relaxed. 'That's a deal. I was hoping to meet the guys for lunch at Downyflake.'

After they strung the lights on the evergreen, Sebastian walked into town to meet his friends. Nicole brought out her beloved old ornaments, set them on the floor, and evaluated them. She was in a new stage of her life, this was the biggest tree she'd ever had, and she wanted it to be the most glorious. She hurried into her car and drove to Marine Home Center.

In the housewares section of the shop, 'White Christmas' played softly over the sound system. Christmas baubles filled the shelves, each more adorable than the other. Mothers with children knelt down to discuss which miniature crèche scene to purchase for their houses. Honestly, the ornaments became cleverer every year, Nicole thought, in a frenzy of confusion over how to limit herself to just a few choices. Penguins on ice skates, red-nosed reindeer, trains with wheels like red and white peppermint candy, airplanes with Snoopy waving and his red scarf flying backward, snowflakes, grinning camels, tiny dolls in white velvet coats with red berries in their hair . . . Oh, Nicole *loved* this season!

She bought lots of decorations, and if she thought she might be going just a wee bit overboard, she remembered Maddox. What fun it would be to have a child in the house for Christmas!

Back home, she listened to a holiday CD while she hung the ornaments. As she worked, she discovered she needed to rearrange the furniture, to push the sofas and chairs away from the tall, bushy tree. Standing back, she wondered if it wasn't just a bit overwhelming. Had she made a mistake? Misjudged? Was the tree too big? Was she just a hopeless cornball with no sense of restraint and elegance?

She resisted hanging one last candy cane, plugged in the small multi-colored lights, and collapsed on the sofa to review her handiwork. It was quite an amazing sight, she thought, bright, joyful, playful . . . absent-mindedly she chewed on the end of the candy cane.

Oh! She was hungry! She'd worked right through lunch. No wonder she had misgivings about the tree. Her blood sugar was low.

Or was the tree *too much*? Would Sebastian's heart sink when he saw it, would he realize with horror that the woman he married lacked all sense of refinement? Nicole worriedly crunched the candy cane.

'I'm home!' Sebastian's voice boomed out as he came in the door, bringing a blast of cold winter air with him.

Nicole glanced up nervously. 'Did you have a nice lunch?'

Sebastian strode across the room, pulled her to her feet, and kissed her soundly.

'My,' she sighed. 'What's that for?'

'That's for the tree,' Sebastian told her. 'You should come out and see it from the street. It's great. I've never seen anything like it.'

She laughed with pleasure. 'It's not too big for this room?'

He studied it. 'It's big. It's so big it reminds me of the trees my parents used to put up when I was a little boy.' His face softened. 'So long ago.'

'Oh, you've still got a bit of little boy in you,' Nicole teased him, nuzzling his neck.

Sebastian grinned. 'Don't you mean big boy?' he joked.

'Why, Sebastian.' She hugged him, turning her head sideways to gaze at the tree, feeling warm and loved and smug and absolutely brimming with holiday spirit.

Chapter Eight

The ferry from Hyannis to Nantucket was like a game of bump-'em cars Maddox once had been on at a friend's birthday party. The big boat raised up, then smashed down, and waves slammed into the giant boat's hull, making it shudder. Maddox thought it was *awesome*.

His mommy didn't like it much, though. She lay on a bench, wrapped in her coat, hands clutching her belly.

'Let's go up top, Mad Man,' James said, taking his son by the hand.

This was awesome, too. Maddox rarely got alone time with his daddy, who was always working. Maddox felt secure with his tiny hand tucked inside

Daddy's large warm hand. They went up the stairs, taking care because of the heaving boat, and stood by the high windows looking out at the water. His daddy lifted him up into his arms so Maddox could see better, and Maddox inhaled deeply of his daddy's masculine scent, his aftershave lotion, his wool sweater, his cotton turtleneck. Maddox wrapped one arm around his father's neck and leaned against him slightly, so he could feel the raspy skin on his face.

'Maybe we'll see a whale out here,' his daddy said.

'How do they stay warm?' Maddox asked.

James explained, 'The animals and fish that live in the water have different bodies from human beings. They can breathe in the water, and they never get cold. But they can't breathe in the air like we do, and our air is much too dry for them.'

Maddox marveled at this thought. He gazed out into the waves, which were dark blue, crested with frothy white, rolling relentlessly toward the boat to crash into the sides, making the boat shiver and the waves explode into fizzy silver suds.

He tightened his hold on his father. The world was so big, and this view of it on such a cold December day made him feel very small. In preschool, he'd seen a picture book depicting Santa Claus traveling to an island in his sleigh. The sleigh was drawn by porpoises, seals, walruses, and whales, and it skipped over the top of the waves while Santa held the reins.

The book had made Maddox uneasy. Santa was supposed to fly through the air. Maddox had seen pictures of the sleigh in other books. What did Santa do with the reindeer when he used the porpoises? And if he crossed the water with the sea creatures, what happened when he got to the island? If what his father said was right, porpoises couldn't breathe on dry land, so how did Santa get up to the chimneys of the houses? It was hard to understand how the world worked, especially on an island.

A funny *yip* interrupted Maddox's thoughts. Looking down, he saw a yellow puppy tugging the laces of his daddy's sneakers.

A lady with gray hair and earrings shaped like Christmas trees rushed over. 'I'm so sorry,' she apologized pleasantly. She picked up the puppy and held him in her arms. 'This is Chips,' she told Maddox and his father. Holding the puppy's paw, she waved it in a hello gesture. 'We're taking Chips to give to our granddaughter for Christmas.' Seeing Maddox's face, she asked, 'Would you like to pet him?'

Maddox nodded solemnly.

'I'll put him on the floor. You can play with him. Be careful, he bites, well, not actually *bites*, he nibbles, he's got his baby teeth, and he's only two months old. He doesn't mean to hurt.'

James set Maddox down on the floor next to the puppy. Maddox held out his hand. Chips licked it and wriggled all over. Maddox patted the puppy, then scratched behind his ears. Chips turned circles and flopped over onto his back, exposing his fat white belly. Maddox rubbed it and Chips wiggled in ecstasy, kicking his hind legs as if he were riding a bike. Maddox giggled.

'Here.' The lady handed Maddox a short rope. 'He loves to tug.'

The second Maddox took the rope, Chips snatched the other end in his sharp white puppy teeth and yanked so hard he pulled it right out of Maddox's hand.

'Hey!' Maddox yelled, reaching out to capture the rope, but Chips ran away. Giggling, Maddox chased after him. They went only a few steps when Chips tripped on his own feet and somersaulted head over heels, never once letting go of the rope. But Maddox caught up with him and clutched the rope, and the boy and the puppy began to tug. It was so much fun. Maddox laughed and laughed. The puppy let go of the rope and actually jumped onto Maddox, who was on his knees. Chips sort of latched onto Maddox with his puppy paws and began licking Maddox's face all over, as if Maddox tasted delicious. Maddox fell over on his back, delirious with happiness as the puppy's wet pink tongue slurped his eyelids, his cheeks, and once right up his nose!

'Maddox, darling? Why are you on the floor?' His mommy stood at the top of the stairs, clutching the railing, pale and anxious. 'Are you all right?'

The older lady quickly bent down and lifted Chips off Maddox. 'Hello,' she said to Kennedy. 'I'm sorry, I was just letting Chips play with the child. I'm afraid I'm rather boring for the poor puppy.'

His mommy smiled. 'That's so kind of you. Maddox would love to have a puppy. I'm just not sure I could deal with one now . . .' She put her hand on her belly.

The older lady nodded her head. 'Wiser to take your time. You can always get a puppy later.'

Maddox glanced back and forth between the older woman and his mommy, who seemed to be communicating without saying all the words.

James hefted Maddox into his arms. 'Look,' he said, pointing. 'We're almost there. I see the lighthouse. Soon we'll be nice and warm, and Nicole will serve us a delicious meal.'

'Goodbye,' the woman said, waving Chips's paw.

Maddox's daddy said, 'Kennedy, let me help you go back down the stairs. You shouldn't have climbed them by yourself, not with the boat rocking so much.'

Supporting Maddox with one arm, and Maddox's mommy with the other, his strong daddy carefully escorted them down the steps to the main cabin. They were almost on the island!

Chapter Nine

Kennedy was so blissed-out she was miserable.

After their arrival yesterday afternoon, her father had helped James carry in the bags. To Kennedy's surprise, the room at the back of the house behind the kitchen had been transformed into a bedroom. This way, Nicole had pointed out, Kennedy wouldn't have to climb the stairs. The room had been called the birthing room when the house was built back in the eighteen hundreds, because it was near the kitchen and easy to keep warm. When her parents were married, this room was the TV room.

Kennedy had worried that Maddox would be afraid to be on the second floor, so far away from his parents, but Nicole had decorated the spare bedroom in a spaceship theme, with posters of rockets and a bedspread printed with comets. All around the ceiling, small stickers of stars, planets, and meteors glowed gently in the dark. A bookshelf held building blocks, children's books, and tractors, dump trucks, and fire engines. Maddox loved it. He immediately called it *his* room.

Last night, Nicole had served a delicious meal, even though the calorie count was over the moon. Pork loin with apples and onions, roasted squash risotto, broccolini, beets with orange sauce, and fresh, home-made, whole wheat bread with butter. She'd bought the kind of veggie burgers Kennedy had requested and cooked those for Maddox, who ate all of them, as well as his broccolini and beets.

This morning, Nicole and Kennedy's father had taken Maddox out for breakfast in town, allowing Kennedy and James to sleep late and spend time alone in bed snuggling, something they had been unable to do for months.

Then, because the day was sunny and surprisingly mild, her father and Nicole had suggested having a picnic way out on Great Point, where Maddox could see the lighthouse and the big fat seals who lounged about on the shore, grunting, lolling, and snorting.

The last thing Kennedy wanted to do was to be bounced around in a four-wheel-drive vehicle along a sandy beach path. Her lower back was twinging with such force she felt like a grunting seal herself.

When she begged off going, to her utter amazement, Nicole had cooed, 'Of course you should stay home. Why don't you settle on the sofa? I'll have your father build you a nice fire. I've got a stack of magazines and light reading you might enjoy. Go on, put your feet up. Get comfy.'

Kennedy had lowered her bulk onto the sofa and raised her heavy feet up to a pillow. Instant ecstasy. Before she left, Nicole brought in a tray. On it were a plate of sandwiches, a bowl of carrots and red pepper strips, and to Kennedy's childish delight, a selection of homemade Christmas cookies. Gingerbread men and women with white icing faces. Irresistible sugar cookies with snowy icing covered with multicolored sprinkles shaped like reindeer, wreaths, and angels. Finally – in a white pot decorated with green holly and red berries – there was steaming, rich, milky, homemade hot chocolate to pour into a matching mug.

Kennedy's father, James, and Maddox were hefting a picnic basket, several wool blankets, and a couple of thermoses out to the Jeep Grand Cherokee.

'Bye, Mommy,' Maddox called.

Nicole came back into the living room, wearing jeans, a green Christmas sweater with a snowman on

57

it, and hiking boots. 'All set?' In her hands she held a red and green plaid down blanket trimmed in satin. 'I'll just tuck this in around you.' She fluttered the cover over Kennedy's legs and nudged it in around Kennedy's feet. She scooted the coffee table close, just within Kennedy's reach. 'Anything else?'

'This is great,' Kennedy admitted grudgingly. 'Thank you.'

'Bye, then. See you in a few hours.' Nicole fluttered her fingers and left.

A few hours? A few hours alone in the house with cookies, hot chocolate, and peace and quiet? Kennedy almost wept with relief.

Although . . . something about being tucked in with a blanket unsettled her, brought up memories from the far distant past that filled her with a melancholy longing. Now she was the one who made sure her child was covered with a blanket, but there had been times, she could almost remember, like reaching out through a fog, when her own mother had fluttered a blanket down over her.

Katya hadn't ever cared much for the messiness of motherhood. She'd always had babysitters, or nannies, and of course, housekeepers. Kennedy's father was always working. From an early age, Kennedy was encouraged to be a good girl, a 'big girl' – meaning no fussing, no running, no whining.

Kennedy worried that she wasn't a natural mother. She never felt the rush of exultation when Maddox was born that she'd read other mothers had. True, she'd had an epidural, which Katya had advised her to have, in order to avoid the pain of labor and birth that, Katya said, would savage Kennedy. Even with an epidural, Kennedy was shattered for days, which stretched into weeks and months. When Maddox was about seven months old, he started sleeping all night, and after that Kennedy very nearly felt like a normal human being. But when he started crawling and toddling, her fears for him, the need for constant vigilance, the shrieks he sent out when he fell, wiped her out all over again.

She loved him more than her life. He was her joy, her angel, her darling boy. After he was a bit more steady, she and Maddox had entered a kind of honeymoon period, when they had such fun together. He was her darling pal.

It was during that spell when she submitted to James's desire for another child. She had prayed for a girl, but the ultrasound tech said it was another boy. Kennedy tried to be content with that. Certainly it made James feel manly, as if every cell in his body was masculine.

This pregnancy had been as difficult as the first. Morning sickness came early and lasted for months, spiraling nausea through her system day and night. Even though she scarcely ate, the baby grew inside her as if her umbilical cord were an enormous beanstalk attached to a giant. She was uncomfortable, awkward, blotchy, waddly, and incontinent. *Cranky*.

Now she had this dreadful week to get through with her father and his new gushy wife. Nicole had never had children, she probably had no idea of the difficulties of keeping a four-year-old boy amused and under control. Kennedy was terrified that Nicole would feed Maddox so much sugar he'd never sleep. Plus, the environment Nicole had provided – the huge tree, the toy crèche, the stockings hanging from the mantel – they would overstimulate her already active son, causing him to spin out of control.

Kennedy wanted to go home. She wanted this Christmas fuss to be over and done with. She wanted Maddox back in preschool and her days quiet and calm, so she could sleep and rest up for the coming baby.

Although, Kennedy admitted to herself as she poured a cup of hot chocolate and nibbled a sugar cookie, this wasn't so bad. Pretty nice, actually.

So, fine. Nicole was obviously doing her best. That didn't mean that Kennedy had to like her or be glad that her father had gone and *married* her.

Why couldn't her father understand that women

had midlife crises just like men? Obviously, Katya had been bored with her husband of thirty years and had just needed some excitement. Perhaps Katya was beginning to feel — not *old*, Katya would never be old — but less alluring than usual. After all, Katya's daughter was grown up and married now, and Katya had become a *grandmother* with its connotations of gray hair in a bun and flapping upper arms. Kennedy totally *knew* her mother had run off with Alonzo to prove to herself that she was still desirable. Instead of divorcing Katya, Kennedy's father should have gone after her, wooed her, and won her back. He still could, if he hadn't married that damned Nicole.

What was so great about Nicole, anyway, that Sebastian had to marry her? She was pretty, but not beautiful like Katya, and she was, okay, not fat, but definitely plump. She wasn't classy, couldn't play tennis or sail, didn't know any of Sebastian's friends. Why couldn't Kennedy's father just have had a frivolous fling with her and then gotten back together with Katya?

Maybe he still could.

Maybe this week could illuminate for Sebastian how awful it was to be without his beautiful, sophisticated, silky ex-wife.

Maybe Kennedy could demonstrate to her father how hard it was for her to be in this house, her mother's house really, with Nicole the Interloper, and Sebastian would be overcome with guilt for marrying Nicole, and divorce her and remarry Katya!

This would take some cunning on Kennedy's part.

Kennedy ate another gingerbread cookie. She finished her mug of hot chocolate. She reached for a magazine, relaxed back against the cushions, and read about the loves of Hollywood celebrities and pregnancies of princesses until her eyes drifted closed and a soft slumber possessed her.

Chapter Ten

Nicole sat in the backseat with Maddox during the long bumpy ride out to Great Point. Seb's Jeep Grand Cherokee easily churned through the deep sand, tossing the passengers up and down, which made Maddox shriek with glee. The day was full of wind and surf and clouds blowing over the sun, sending a glancing, dancing brilliant light across the beach and into their eyes.

Sebastian stopped the Jeep near the lighthouse. Only a few yards away, scores of harbor seals lounged on the sand.

Maddox giggled as they stepped out onto the beach. 'I want to pet one,' he told his daddy.

'Darling, they bite,' Nicole warned. 'You can't go near them. They're wild creatures.'

They strolled along the beach, picking up shells, staying far away from the winter waves crashing on the shore. Nearby, a clan of the larger horsehead seals bobbed in the water like a gang of curious wet gorillas. James lifted Maddox up on his shoulders so the boy could see a fishing boat anchored in the distance, among the white-capped waves.

'I'm hungry!' Maddox declared.

'Then let's eat,' Nicole replied easily.

Sitting on a picnic blanket, they munched lunch while watching the seals, who muttered and oinked like sea pigs. At one point, two seals got into a snorting argument, a comic scene that made everyone laugh.

After lunch, they walked through the dunes up to the sixty-foot-high, whitewashed stone lighthouse. They returned to the Jeep and bumped back down the sand to the area called Coskata, where to Maddox's great delight, they spotted a snowy owl, pristine white and immensely arrogant, seated on a scrub oak. They tromped through a wooded glade to find Nicole's favorite tree, an ancient beech with arms stretching out like elephants' trunks. It was perfect for climbing, so Maddox scrambled up onto one of the lower branches, and Sebastian took his photo. They continued on the narrow path until they arrived at a pond where a white heron stalked among the marshy grasses. Maddox helped Nicole fill a bucket with mussels they picked from the shoreline and they scampered about on a fallen tree trunk. Sebastian led them to a midden, a gathering of broken shells left from a long-ago Native American tribe. He told Maddox about how the early Americans had lived here, eating fish and berries, drinking water from the ponds, covered with goose grease in the summer to protect them from mosquito bites. Maddox's eyes went wide with amazement.

In the late afternoon, when the sun was beginning to set, Sebastian steered the SUV off the sand and onto the paved road leading back to town. He yawned. Beside him, in the passenger seat, James yawned. In the backseat, both Nicole and Maddox caught the contagious reflex and yawned so hard they squeaked.

'Close your eyes,' Nicole urged Maddox. 'Take a nap.'

The boy didn't need to be invited twice. He sagged into his rented car seat and was immediately asleep.

So much fresh air and exercise. Nicole leaned her head back against the seat and closed her own eyes, congratulating herself for having prepared a casserole for their dinner tonight. She'd steam the mussels for a first course with melted butter, but that would take only a few minutes. She hoped Kennedy had

had a restful day and would be pleased by Nicole's efforts.

Sebastian brought the Jeep to a stop by the two air pumps stationed by the side of the road just past the Trustees of Reservations cabin. He took the tire pressure gauge out of the glove compartment. Air had to be let out of the tires for easy driving on the sand, and Maddox had been fascinated by the way his grandfather made the air hiss out by pressing a rock on the valve stem. Nicole wasn't surprised when Maddox sprang awake from his light doze.

'Want to help me put the air back in?' Sebastian asked his grandson.

Maddox eagerly unfastened his seat belt and jumped out of the car. James filled the tires on the right side, Sebastian and Maddox took the ones on the left. Then they buckled up and drove away toward town.

Back at the house, Nicole was delighted to discover Kennedy with rosy cheeks and bright eyes.

'Thank you, Daddy.' Kennedy waddled up to Sebastian and gave him a hug. 'I had the best rest I've had in weeks.'

Nicole waited for Kennedy to thank her, too. Instead, Kennedy squatted down, bracing herself with one hand on a wall, to hug Maddox.

'Did you have fun, honey-bunny?'

'Mommy, I saw seals! And a rabbit! And an owl!

And I put air in a tire!' Maddox was almost stammering with excitement.

'Tell me all about it in the bath,' Kennedy suggested. She held out a hand and her husband hoisted her to her feet. 'I'll take Maddox up for a nice long bath. You guys can enjoy drinks before dinner.'

With her son yammering away, Kennedy slowly went up the stairs.

Nicole carried the bucket of mussels into the kitchen, trying not to mind that Kennedy had not even bothered to say hello to her. She set the bucket in the sink, washed her hands, and went into the living room to gather up the plate of cookies and the hot chocolate. The cookies, she noticed, had disappeared. The magazines were scattered over the floor. The blanket was balled up, hanging half over the arm of the sofa. Crumbs littered the sofa and the carpet, as well as a used napkin and a few used tissues.

At the sight of the tissues wadded up on the floor, Nicole sat down with a sigh and took a moment to compose herself.

Really? she thought. Did Kennedy expect Nicole not only to provide all the meals and snacks, but also to pick up after her like a servant? True, Kennedy was bulky with her pregnancy, but she was standing up when they arrived home. Surely Kennedy could have carried her used tissues to the waste basket in the bathroom. Sebastian had told Nicole what a neat freak Katya was, and Nicole was certain Katya had passed along her tidiness to Kennedy, so this clutter Kennedy had left was more than a mess – it was a message.

I don't like you, and I never will. Was that the point of the lumpy tissues, the strewn magazines? What on earth had Nicole done to warrant such animosity? She knew Kennedy wanted her parents to get back together, but Kennedy was not demented, she had to realize her mother had been hooked up with the gorgeous Alonzo for years.

Nicole gathered up the magazines and patted them into a neat pile on the coffee table. With thumb and forefinger, she pinched up the used tissues and napkin and dropped them on the tray next to the empty cookie plate, mug, and pot. Nicole was slow to anger, but she was on her way now. She took a moment to feast her eyes on the Christmas tree, trying to absorb its gleaming serenity into her mood.

She had never had children, but she believed that if Kennedy were her child, she would confront her. She would scold her. At the least, she would force Kennedy to recognize her existence and her attempts to make this a pleasant holiday for everyone.

Sebastian stuck his head into the room. 'James and I are going to have a drink. Could I fix you one?'

Nicole relaxed her gritted teeth. 'A glass of red wine would be excellent right now,' she replied. Perhaps that would calm her down, put her back in the Christmas spirit, and prevent her from doing or saying something she would later regret.

Chapter Eleven

Maddox woke early, as he always did. He played with the cool toys in his room as quietly as he could, because his mommy needed her sleep for the baby. He looked at the picture books. He stood at the window staring out at Granddad's backyard. It was kind of interesting, with its toolshed and wooden picnic table and benches. If he tipped over the benches, and maybe if he could find a big cardboard box, he could make a fort like his friend Jeremy had. Cool!

He trotted out of his room, down the stairs, through the hall to the kitchen and the mudroom with the back door.

'Going somewhere, sport?' Granddad sat at the kitchen table with a cup of coffee and a newspaper.

Nicole was at the other end of the table, drinking coffee and making a list on a pad of paper. They were both wearing pajamas, robes, and furry slippers.

Maddox requested, politely, 'May I please play in the backyard?'

'I don't see why not,' Granddad answered.

'Hang on,' said Nicole. 'You need to get dressed first, Maddox. You'll freeze in your pajamas. Have you been to the bathroom yet?'

Maddox slumped. He'd thought Nicole was different, but she was just like the other adults, full of rules.

Nicole rose from the table and held out her hand. 'Let me help you get dressed. I'll pick out your warmest pants.'

Maddox stared at the door to the room where his mommy and daddy slept.

'We won't wake your parents,' Nicole whispered. 'We'll be quiet as two little mice.'

She was as good as her word. She tiptoed with Maddox up the stairs. They didn't speak as she helped him dress and use the bathroom. They went like pirates back down the stairs, and no one woke up.

In the kitchen, Nicole asked, 'Want some breakfast before you go outside, Maddox?'

'No, thank you. I want to make a fort out of the picnic table and benches.' He thought he might as well just come out with the truth in case they didn't like that sort of thing, their yard getting all messed up.

Nicole surprised him. 'Good idea. We've got some folding lawn chairs in the shed that will make a good doorway on the ends. I'll get them out for you after I get dressed.'

Maddox eyed her skeptically. He wasn't sure about those lawn chairs. He wasn't sure he wanted his idea tampered with.

'Boots,' Nicole said. 'Coat, cap, and mittens.' She retrieved the items from the hooks in the mudroom and put them on Maddox, a cumbersome process he hated. He was never cold and the extra padding made it harder to move. But he allowed himself to be yanked, tugged, and zipped, because he understood the adults were right.

Finally, Nicole unlocked the back door. Maddox stepped onto the back porch.

'Stay in the backyard, now, Maddox,' Nicole warned. 'Don't go away, promise?'

'I promise.'

The back porch was like a room without walls. It had a swing hanging from the ceiling, and a wicker sofa and two wicker armchairs. The wide steps going down had railings on each side. Maddox hung on to them as he went, his slightly-too-big boots hampering him, making him clumsy.

She handed him a pair of field glasses. Puzzled, he turned them around in his hands. Nicole knelt down and demonstrated how to use them. She helped him turn the round knob until the view went clear.

Maddox was speechless. This was the most excellent fort toy he had ever seen. He raced away, binoculars in hand, ready to enter his fantasy world.

Chapter Twelve

Nicole returned to the kitchen, shivering slightly. She'd gone out to the shed without a coat or hat and the day was frosty.

Sebastian rose from the table. 'I'll get shaved and dressed and bring in more firewood.' He smacked a kiss on her lips.

Nicole poured her second cup of coffee and stood at the window, keeping an eye on Maddox as he dragged a floral cushion from the shed to his fort. Hearing a shuffling noise, she turned to see Kennedy coming into the kitchen, wrapped in a puffy pink robe that couldn't quite close over her belly.

'Good morning, Kennedy,' Nicole said brightly.

Kennedy collapsed in a chair. 'I hope you've got bacon and eggs for breakfast. I'm starved.'

Nicole stared. She counted to ten. She recalled her years on the wards as a nurse, when patients were too ill to be polite, unable to do more than mumble. Kennedy was only pregnant, not sick, but still, this was a state Nicole had never endured, so she decided to be kind.

'I'll be glad to make you some, Kennedy,' Nicole offered.

Kennedy buried her face in her hands.

Alarmed, Nicole came closer to the table. 'Kennedy, do you feel all right?'

Kennedy didn't raise her head. 'I told you. I'm hungry.'

Without another word, Nicole set about microwaving bacon and scrambling eggs. She shaved slivers of cheddar into the eggs and added a pinch of basil. She squeezed oranges and set a fresh glass of juice in front of Kennedy. She placed a napkin and utensils near Kennedy's place.

She had to admit, Kennedy had stamina. Nicole could never sit in steaming silence while another woman cooked for her.

Gosh. Maybe Kennedy was truly ill. Worry spurted into Nicole's chest.

'Good morning, gorgeous!' James came out of the

guest bedroom, smelling of soap and aftershave. 'Morning, Nicole.'

'Hi, James. Would you like some eggs and bacon? I'm fixing some for Kennedy.'

To Nicole's delighted surprise, James gave her a quick one-armed hug. 'The answer is yes.' He poured himself a cup of coffee. 'Where's Wonder Boy?'

'Look out the window.'

'Ha! A fort! I remember building one like that as a boy. Is it okay with you that he's creating havoc in your yard?'

'Of course. He's having fun.'

'Where's Sebastian?' asked James.

'Right here.' Sebastian came into the kitchen, fully dressed. 'Hi, James. Hey, Kabey.' He used his old pet name for his daughter.

Kennedy lifted a beaming face to her father. 'Hi, Daddy.'

'How do you feel?'

'Like a wheelbarrow full of potatoes,' Kennedy told her father.

'You don't look it,' Sebastian lied, sitting down next to her.

Nicole placed the plate of eggs and bacon in front of Kennedy.

Kennedy stared ruefully down at the food. 'Mommy always used to serve such *healthy* meals,' she said

mournfully. 'Fruit for breakfast, with granola and raisins and dried cranberries.'

Nicole stood very still. Her mind raced. Why was Kennedy so obviously setting her up? Kennedy had asked for bacon and eggs, and now that she had them, she wanted fruit and granola? Food was not the issue here, clearly. Nicole would not rise to the bait.

Forcing a smile, Nicole asked, 'Kennedy, would you prefer fruit and granola? We have both.'

'I don't want to be any trouble,' Kennedy pouted.

'No trouble at all,' Nicole purred. Reaching out, she moved the plate of bacon and eggs from Kennedy's spot to James's. 'Here, James, why don't you have these?'

'Great, thanks.' James picked up his knife and fork.

Smoothly but quickly, like Martha Stewart on ice skates, Nicole took out a bowl, a box of granola, and a spoon. She set them before Kennedy. She poured skim milk into a pitcher and set it next to the bowl.

Plucking a banana from the fruit bowl in the middle of the table, Nicole extended it to Kennedy. 'Would you like to slice this onto your granola?' *Round one to me*, Nicole thought.

Kennedy nearly quivered with stifled indignation. Her eyes slid over to her husband, happily stuffing the rich creamy eggs into his mouth.

'Oh,' Kennedy bleated, pressing her belly. 'I feel so awful.'

'Maybe you should go lie down,' Sebastian suggested.

'Try to eat a little,' Nicole urged in honeyed tones. 'Your blood sugar is low in the morning.'

With a heavy sigh, Kennedy poured the milk, sliced the banana, and ate the granola.

'Feel better?' Nicole inquired sweetly.

Kennedy ignored her. 'Daddy, would you take me shopping like you did when I was young?'

'Sure, honey, but I don't think there are any maternity shops on the island.'

'I don't need maternity clothes, silly daddy,' Kennedy laughed. 'I'm thinking some nice winter boots, maybe a purse . . . and I can always use jewelry, of course.'

'Kennedy, you little minx,' James teased, 'why don't you wait and see what you get for Christmas?'

'Because I want to be with my daddy,' Kennedy cooed.

'Get some clothes on, princess,' Sebastian said. 'I'll take you wherever you want to go.'

Kennedy threw her arms around Sebastian. 'Oh, thank you, Daddy. And will you take me out to lunch, too? Just you and me?'

Sebastian gave his winsome daughter a doting glance. 'Of course. Where do you want to eat?'

'Oh, I don't care,' Kennedy told him. 'Any place where the food is hot and plentiful.' Clumsily, she rose from her chair and shuffled into her bedroom to dress.

In a low voice, Sebastian asked James, 'Do you mind that I'm going off for a private lunch with Kennedy?'

'Are you kidding? This will give me a chance to spend some time alone with Maddox. Besides,' James winked, 'I'm kind of *persona non grata* with Kennedy right now.'

'You are? Why?'

'Because she's pregnant and I'm not.'

The two men shared a conspiratorial chuckle.

Nicole busied herself at the sink, forcing back a gulp of self-pity. Everyone in the house had intimate knowledge of pregnancy and birth. James had, and was sharing it with Kennedy. Sebastian had shared it with Katya. Nicole had never been pregnant. As a nurse, she'd seen babies come into the world, but she'd never had her own.

'Thanks, Nicole.' James brought his empty plate and silverware to the sink. 'That was a treat.'

His friendliness flashed over her like warmth. He headed through the mudroom to the back door. 'Maddox!' he called. 'Hey, Mad Man! Guess what?'

Nicole watched out the window as James squatted down to peer inside the fort. A moment later, Sebastian's arms circled her waist. His breath stirred her hair.

'You don't mind, do you?' he whispered. 'I think

Kennedy will be more receptive to you once she sees you haven't come between us.'

'Of course I don't mind,' Nicole lied. She wanted to burst into tears. She wanted to stamp her foot like a child, crying, *Everyone's leaving me out!* Turning in his arms, she snuggled against him, soaking in the steadiness of his love.

'Daddy, I'm ready!' Kennedy entered the kitchen, chic in her camel-hair coat and tasseled wool hat.

'I'll get my coat,' Sebastian said, going into the front hall.

'I'll go out back and tell Maddox and James goodbye,' Kennedy said. 'Meet you outside.'

Kennedy walked right past Nicole and out the door without saying a word, as if Nicole didn't even exist.

Chapter Thirteen

Kennedy linked her arm through her father's as they strolled down India Street toward town. Her heart swelled with triumph. A light snow was just beginning to fall, its flakes as white and soft as down, making the day even more magical.

'I love being here with you, Daddy.' She leaned her head against his arm for a moment.

'I'm glad, Kabey.'

'Let's look at the windows on Main Street,' Kennedy suggested. 'The merchants are always so clever.' She was subtly steering her father toward lower Main Street and the Jewel of the Isle. Truly, she deserved a diamond for Christmas, and she knew she wasn't getting one from James because she'd had a secret shuffle through

his desk and discovered he was giving her a new Mercedes SUV. Nice, but of course he was being more practical than romantic. He wanted his precious children to ride in safety.

'Oh.' Kennedy gripped her father's arm. 'Stop a minute.'

Concerned, Sebastian inquired, 'Are you having a contraction?'

'Yes. Don't worry. They're just Braxton Hicks. I went into the hospital three times with Maddox, thinking I was starting labor.'

The Nantucket Pharmacy had an ice-skating scene in the window. Fluffy white fleece surrounded a pond made from an oval mirror. Elves, Santa, and a couple of reindeer pirouetted over the shimmering 'ice'. Snow people made of cotton balls with candy eyes, noses, and mouths stood next to Christmas trees adorned with tiny blinking lights. Mrs Santa bent over an open box of chocolates, as if deciding which to choose first.

'Cute,' Sebastian said.

'Adorable. Lucky Mrs Santa. She can eat all the chocolate she wants.'

'Why can't you?' her father asked.

'Daddy! I'm already a whale.' Kennedy tugged on his arm. 'I'm okay now. Let's walk some more.'

A fabulous Icelandic sweater in the window of Peach Tree's caught her eye, but she bypassed it, determined to get her diamond.

'Shall we walk down to Straight Wharf and buy a few wooden toys for Maddox at the Toy Boat?' Sebastian suggested.

Her father was heading them in the perfect direction. She squeezed his arm. 'Good idea.'

In the small fisherman's cottage housing the Toy Boat, Sebastian strode around gleefully, seeming like a kid himself. 'Lighthouses, ferries, sailboats — so much to choose from. What do you think, Kennedy?'

Kennedy started to warn her father not to spoil Maddox, but bit her tongue. What she thought was that she wanted her father to spoil *her*. Why did children get all the goodies? The mommies did all the work. Sure, James had Maddox today, but most days of the year, her husband escaped their chaotic house wearing suit and tie, heading to the sophisticated adult world while Kennedy wrestled Maddox into the car for preschool then returned to the grocery shopping, laundry, and dishes.

She could understand now why her mother had employed a live-in nanny. Kennedy did have several good babysitters, and a cleaning service that came in twice a week. The laundry did James's shirts. They ate out or brought in takeout several times a week, especially since this second pregnancy. Compared to many others, she was spoiled, but she certainly didn't *feel* spoiled.

Kennedy loved Maddox with all her heart. He was

the light of her life. But nothing had prepared her for the noise, the mess, the constant, relentless neediness of a child.

Thank goodness Maddox enjoyed the preschool he attended in the morning. In the afternoon she tried to coax him into napping, but he was a living typhoon. In a month, she'd be saddled with two children, a baby who wouldn't sleep at night and a boy who tore around all day.

And yet . . . something deep within her cherished all this. Kennedy admired her mother intensely and wanted to be just like her, except perhaps a bit less perfect, which heaven knew was easy to achieve. Kennedy remembered the messes – real and emotional – she'd made as a child and how her nanny had consoled her and helped Kennedy clean them up. There'd been something so warm, so real, so *bonding* about those times. She wanted to provide that for her own children, even if she did it imperfectly, and oh boy, did she do it imperfectly.

If only someone would understand. No one ever praised mothers for the tedious work of child caring. No one ever gave a mother an award for not losing her temper ten times a day or for cajoling a kid to eat his vegetables. James tried to sympathize, but he was preoccupied with his work.

Perhaps that was why Kennedy wanted her father

to give her something, a spontaneous surprise to show her that *she* was the light of *his* life. Something like – a diamond?

Returning along Main Street, they passed Jewel of the Isle.

'Oh,' Kennedy gasped. 'Isn't that pretty!'

Sebastian paused, grateful for an opportunity to set the bags full of toys down and relax his hands. 'What, sweetheart?'

'That diamond Christmas tree brooch. So sweet.'

Sebastian peered in the window. 'It's nice.' Suddenly an idea struck him. 'Let's go in, Kennedy.'

Inside, the shop sparkled with gemstones, silver, and gold. Kelli Trainor approached them. 'Hello, Mr Somerset. Merry Christmas.'

'Merry Christmas, Kelli. Could you tell me, how much is that Christmas tree brooch in the window?'

Kellie lifted the pin out and set it, in its black velvet box, on the glass counter. She named a price.

Sebastian asked Kennedy, 'I think that's reasonable, don't you? The diamonds are quite clear.'

'It's gorgeous, Daddy,' Kennedy gushed. She was almost fainting. It was a Christmas fairy tale. Her father had sensed her wish without a word, almost as if they had ESP!

'I'll take it.' Sebastian removed his wallet from his pocket and slid out a credit card.

would you like that wrapped?' Kelli asked.

Kennedy opened her mouth to suggest they pin it on her coat instead, but before she could speak, her father nodded.

'Yes, please, Kelli.' He beamed when he looked over at Kennedy. 'Thanks for suggesting it, Kennedy. Nicole will be so surprised. I never think to buy her romantic presents. She's been working so hard trying to make this a perfect holiday for everyone. I can't wait to see her face when she opens the package on Christmas morning.'

Kennedy's mouth fell open. Her throat closed tight with dismay.

'That's so sweet,' Kelli said, filling the awkward silence.

'Next—' Sebastian's chest swelled with satisfaction as he tucked the wrapped package in with the others.

'Yes, Daddy?' Kennedy widened her eyes innocently.

'Where shall we have lunch? Someplace cozy. The wind's whipping the snow around.'

Kennedy trudged next to her father in silence as they headed to the Brotherhood of Thieves. She was blind to the holiday-bright windows. Her father hummed 'White Christmas,' totally unaware of the disappointment steaming off her. She wanted to stop right there on the brick sidewalk next to the damned

Christmas tree, throw her head back, and t
Everything was wrong. This holiday sucked. She v
a warthog of a woman with a belly that weighed
down her every move. She couldn't look sexy for
her husband, she couldn't even look pretty, and when
she tried to look winsome for her own father, what
did he do? He bought diamonds not for his own
daughter who was carrying his second grandchild, but
for his new wife, who wouldn't even care about them.
Who certainly wouldn't know how to wear them!
Nicole was so more a rhinestone person, she didn't
have the elegance to appreciate diamonds. What a
waste. While Kennedy, at a time in her life when she
could use some affection and pampering and *gratitude*
didn't even get a stupid silver bracelet!

Did Nicole have some kind of psychological hold
over her father? Did Nicole plant drugs in his coffee?
She was way less attractive than Katya, she had no
sense of style, she was like a cleaning woman who
got to sit with the family, and Sebastian had bought
her diamonds? Kennedy wanted to shriek.

'Here we are.' Sebastian ushered his daughter into
the brick-walled bistro. 'After we eat, maybe you'll
have the energy to look at boots.'

'Boots,' Kennedy muttered.

The hostess appeared and seated them in the front
room next to the heartening warmth of the fireplace.

They removed their coats, settled in, and ordered. Sebastian remarked, 'You seem upset.'

Kennedy bit her lower lip. 'I guess . . . I didn't realize you were so . . . enamored of Nicole.'

Her father threw back his head and laughed. 'Honey, Nicole is my wife. I would certainly hope I'd be enamored of her.' He gave Kennedy a concentrated gaze. 'But you're not pleased about this?'

She lowered her eyes and played with her napkin, folding it in different shapes as she talked. 'I want you and Mom to get back together.'

'Oh, Kabey, that's not going to happen. Be realistic, Kennedy. Your mother left me for Alonzo—'

'But they're not married!' Kennedy protested.

Sebastian shrugged. 'Katya probably won't marry again. Your mother likes to have things her own way. As you are now aware, marriage is full of compromises. Come on, Kennedy, you've seen Katya. She's completely fine without me. She's got her own apartment where Alonzo can visit, but it's her place, and she doesn't want it messed up. She's almost sixty, after all. She deserves to spoil herself for a while. So do I, for that matter. I worked hard, providing for my family. Your mother worked hard, raising you and keeping house. Now we want to enjoy life, be free, even a bit silly, before we end up in our rocking chairs.'

Kennedy gripped her father's hand. 'Daddy, you're not *old*!'

'I'm not young, either. I'm healthy. And now, thanks to Nicole, I'm happy. That's a lot.'

Kennedy wanted to appeal prettily, 'Don't *I* make you happy?' but at that moment the waiter arrived with their meals.

'It means the world to me that James is such a nice man,' Sebastian said as he picked up his fork. 'He loves you and Maddox. That's obvious. That's the best gift any father can have, a good, trustworthy, loving son-in-law.'

Kennedy conceded reluctantly, 'Yes. James's great.'

'I wish you could learn to like Nicole,' Sebastian continued. 'She's a wonderful person, and she would love to be part of your life.'

'But she's not my mom,' Kennedy reminded him.

'True. Nicole is completely different from Katya. She's not as concerned about style, she's a bit more into politics, she's a nurse, and she likes being part of the community. You know your mother, Kennedy. Katya always wanted to be seen as being *above* the community. Better than.'

This was true, but Kennedy protested, 'Please don't say negative things about my mother. It hurts my feelings.'

'I'm sorry, Kennedy. Let's change the subject. What did you get James for Christmas?'

'Just some outdoor gear ordered from catalogs,' she replied. 'After all, I'm about to give him another son.'

'I'm glad you brought that up. I feel kind of lousy, joining your mother and James at the hospital and ;aving out Nicole.'

This conversation was SO not going the way she'd planned! 'She can hang out in the waiting room with Alonzo,' Kennedy suggested.

Sebastian patted her hand. 'I think you need a nap.'

Kennedy wanted to say she needed a diamond brooch, but she kept her silence and focused on her food. If only she weren't so tired with this pregnancy, she'd have better ideas about how to get her parents back together, or at least how to get rid of Nicole. But her father was right. She was tired. She'd think more clearly after a nap.

Because she wasn't finished yet.

Whatever happened, Kennedy suddenly wondered, to Cinderella's father and the wicked stepmother after Cinderella married the prince?

Chapter Fourteen

The snow was coming down quickly now, coating the lawn with a layer of pristine white. Snix was cold, and he was hungry.

He was also curious. This morning he'd hidden in a hedge to watch a boy build a peculiar house, a kind of cave, perfectly dog-sized. His father had come out to help him reinforce it with layers from cardboard boxes, covered with some old blankets, then wrapped around and around the outside with duct tape.

Now the boy and his father had gone. It seemed all the humans had gone.

Snix trotted to the funny makeshift house. Easing his way between two lawn chairs tilted on their sides he entered.

It was warm. Cushions covered the floor. No snow got in. It would be the best place to sleep at night!

But as hard as he sniffed, he could find no food in here. Reluctantly, he left the warm cave for the cold snowy outer world. Time for another food quest. Before he ventured away, he peed on a bush, the side of the garage, and the side of the house, so he'd be sure to know where to return.

He headed toward town. Many of the narrower streets were still and empty, the owners of the houses away in their winter homes, the windows dark, the trash barrels scentless. He found his way to Centre Street, where the aroma of bacon drifted from the Jared Coffin House like a love song, but the trash barrels had special locks on them, probably against marauding cats.

Across the street, Le Languedoc was shut tight. He trotted past the brick town buildings and the Whaling Museum until he came to the most likely place to find food.

Broad Street. Steamboat Wharf. Dog heaven. Taco Taco. Walters gourmet sandwiches to go. A pizza place. A coffee shop. The trash barrels' lids were not so tightly fit, and being this close to the water, the ravaging gulls often did the work of breaking and entering for Snix.

Sure enough, in an alley he found a barrel on its

side, papers and cups spilling out. A group of sky rats were pecking away at the contents.

He hesitated. Gulls were mean. They were almost bigger than Snix. Those beaks were as sharp as knives. His only hope was to fake it, so he charged toward them, barking savagely, showing his white pointed teeth. To his relief, with much irate screeching, the birds flew away.

He'd gotten there in time. Nosing away the papers, he hunted out buns, taco shells, hamburger, and cold fries. His belly swelled. He felt so much better. So much stronger. So much more hopeful.

He ate until he couldn't squeeze another morsel into his body. Replete, his body begged for sleep.

He retraced his steps to the house with the warm cave. People were out on the streets, calling out glee-fully about the snow, elated that it was going to be a white Christmas. Snix wasn't so pleased. He was scared. Still, it swelled his heart to see so many people smiling, chatting, waving, dressed in red, white, and green, their arms full of packages. It made the world seem like a friendlier place.

Near Nantucket Bookworks, a teenage boy noticed Snix. 'Hi, guy,' the kid said, reaching down to scratch Snix between the ears. 'Aren't you a cute little pooch.'

Snix cocked his head, trying to send a message: *Take me home with you.*

A girl came out of the shop, a book bag in her hand. 'Okay,' she said, 'now let's go to Murray's Toggery. I'll get Dad a sweater.' She linked her arm through the boy's and led him away, not even aware of Snix sitting there wagging his tail. The boy walked off.

But the friendly warmth of his touch remained, all through Snix's body.

He continued on his way, back through the maze of narrow lanes, until he found his own scent on a bush. The house had lights on inside, but he heard no sounds of people, so he took a chance and dashed straight into the backyard and through the lawn chairs into the cave.

Oh, it was warm. The cushions were soft. The wind howled but no snow made its way inside. His belly was full. His neck had been scratched. A human had told him he was cute. Curling up in comfort, Snix fell asleep.

Chapter Fifteen

After breakfast, Nicole cleaned the kitchen. Upstairs, she made all the beds. She considered picking up the clothes littering her stepdaughter-in-law's floor and putting them in the laundry basket, because it had to be difficult for Kennedy to bend over. On the other hand, Princess Kennedy might object to Nicole touching her things, so she let them lie. She did a quick run through the house with the vacuum.

As she worked, she longed to wallow in the delicious self-indulgent behavior she once treated herself with as a widow. She could no longer curl up on the sofa shoveling popcorn into her mouth while watching *Terms of Endearment* and weeping so hard she choked

on her popcorn. Sebastian was too elegant to imagine she could behave in such a churlish manner, so she restrained herself. Frankly, she missed it.

She phoned Jilly. 'I'm a pariah in my own house.'

'Poor thing. Come to Mama.'

'I've got too much to do.'

'Nonsense. If they can go out to lunch, so can we. It's snowing, Nicole. Look out the window! We can take a long walk on the beach and let the wind blow away our troubles, then have clam chowder at Met on Main.'

Nicole hesitated.

'Oh, you'd rather stay home and sulk?' Jilly teased. 'I'll meet you at the Hub in ten minutes.'

Putting on her snowboots immediately lifted Nicole's mood. Brown suede with thick rubbery soles, they were lined with white fleece and had red and green tartan laces. She pulled on her puffy red down coat and a red wool hat adorned with a knit green holly leaf, complete with red berry, shouldered her purse, slid on her red mittens and hurried out into the invigorating air.

Jilly was already at the Hub, festive in green wool coat and hand-knit creamy white cap and muffler. She greeted Nicole with a big hug and kiss. 'Let's walk down to Straight Wharf and then over to the town beach.'

'Good idea.' Nicole glanced around. 'People are out shopping.'

'I've done all mine. I've got two duffel bags full of presents to take to Boston when we go for Christmas with the grandchildren.'

'You leave tomorrow?' They passed Peach Tree's. 'Great sweater.'

'I know. Don't tempt me.' They walked on toward the water. 'First thing.'

'I'll miss you,' Nicole said.

'You'll be fine. Christmas is in two days. They leave on the twenty-seventh. You can survive that long.'

Buoyed by her friend's companionship, Nicole thought just maybe she could. 'Maddox is an adorable child, and James is nice. He tries hard to be pleasant to everyone. But I swear Kennedy is on some kind of campaign to make me lose my cool. She's absolutely devious, Jilly.' As they ambled along through the falling snow, Nicole described the morning's breakfast psychodrama with the bacon and eggs.

'You're attributing too much premeditation to her,' Jilly insisted. 'Kennedy's a nice enough girl, as I recall. She's pregnant, remember? Pregnancy makes you irrational. Give her a break.'

'You're right,' Nicole conceded reluctantly. 'I just wish Sebastian would stick up for me more. He always seems to think his daughter is flawless.'

'Typical father,' Jilly said knowingly. 'I can't tell you the times Bob and I have argued over something Stacey's done or wants to do. He always takes her side. I'm always the disciplinarian. But in a few days, Kennedy will go home and you'll have Seb back for yourself.'

Nicole's sigh of satisfaction was cut short. Across the street and down a block, she saw Sebastian and Kennedy leaving the Jewel of the Isle. Sebastian had a small dark green bag in his hand. He linked his arm through his daughter's and carefully escorted her around the corner onto Easy Street.

'Look.' She nudged Jilly with her elbow. 'Sebastian just bought Kennedy some jewelry.'

Jilly spotted the retreating pair. 'It's Christmas, Nicole.'

'Oh, I know! I hate the way I feel, like a sniveling jealous fairy-tale witch. Let's change the subject. Tell me what you're reading.'

Both women were voracious readers. Books kept them talking for the rest of their walk and most of their lunch at Fog Island. When they parted to go their separate ways, Nicole was back in her usual optimistic, level-headed mindset.

In the early afternoon, Maddox and Kennedy took naps while the others lounged in bed or the den, reading and watching television. Kennedy was still sleeping

when Maddox woke, so Nicole, who was in the kitchen, gave him permission to go in the backyard and build a snowman.

'I'm making pumpkin lasagna for tonight,' she told the boy. 'Just as soon as I put it in the oven, I'll come out and join you.'

She helped him don his outdoor gear and watched as the child ran joyfully out into the snowy late afternoon. She sprinkled fresh Parmesan on the lasagna and slid it into the oven. As she rinsed and checked the fresh cranberries she would make for the duck sauce that evening, Sebastian came into the kitchen.

'Something smells appetizing.'

'Good.' Rinsing her hands, Nicole murmured, 'I wish we had two ovens. I have to sort of stagger what I'm cooking with only one.'

Sebastian snorted. 'Sorry, Nicole. Cooking was never one of Katya's passions. One oven was more than enough for her.'

Nicole bit her lip. She didn't enjoy hearing the words Katya and passion come out of her husband's mouth.

As if he'd guessed her thoughts, Sebastian drew Nicole into his arms. 'I hope you realize how grateful I am for all you're doing. Not just the decorating and the cooking, but making the house feel so warm. You've got a gift for perking up people, Nicole.'

For half a second, Nicole considered pointing out

that she certainly didn't please Kennedy. But that would have been churlish, especially with her husband's arms around her. 'I hope I perk you up, Sebastian.'

'Let's go upstairs and I'll show you,' Sebastian murmured into her neck.

Nicole drew away in pretend horror. 'In the daytime? With your family here?' Secretly, she was tickled.

James chose that moment to come into the kitchen from the birthing room. 'Time for a drink yet?' he asked. 'Kennedy's sound asleep.'

'Maddox is out trying to build a snowman,' Nicole told him. 'I promised I'd go help him, but I got delayed with cooking and um, everything.'

James looked out the window. 'Is Mad in the back-yard or the front?'

'The backyard, of course.' Nicole checked her watch. With a playful glance at Sebastian, she said, 'Dinner's ready in about an hour.'

'I'll play with him until then.' James went out the door.

'Alone at last,' Nicole's husband said, pulling her close once more.

Chapter Sixteen

Maddox stood in the backyard with his tongue protruding, trying to catch the flakes of snow that the wind flung into his eyes and up his nose. When his tongue got cold, he decided to go into his fort.

Snow had settled on top of his hideaway. On one side, snow drifted up into a wall. Maddox dropped to his knees and crawled between the lawn chairs into the warm security of his cave.

It was dark inside. He blinked, thinking about this, trying to understand. Back in the real world, the sun had almost set, but some pale rays still illuminated the sky and the brightness of the snow reflected back the shine. In here – with cardboard walls secured by

duct tape wrappings and a ceiling of picnic table wood – no snow entered, and not much light.

After a moment, his eyes adjusted to the dim interior. It was nice and warm compared to the chill outside. Maddox crawled farther in and closed the cardboard flap that served as a door. Now it was supercozy.

Except . . .

Something was in the corner. Something as big as Maddox. Something dark, at least it looked dark, and as Maddox watched, it moved.

Too paralyzed with terror even to squeak, Maddox stared at the lump. A wolf? No, wolves were bigger. A rat? No, rats were smaller. A rabbit? That would be okay, but it wasn't rabbit shaped.

An eye gleamed through the darkness.

Maddox didn't know what to do. Should he pretend to be something not alive, a big rock, for example? Should he try to be friendly? How fast could he exit the cave before whatever it was leapt at him, catching him by his shoe?

The creature stirred. Two eyes shone. It appeared to be in no hurry to eat Maddox. He knew it wasn't a lion or a bear; Daddy said those didn't exist on the island. Perhaps it was a baby deer? But the thing shuffled into a standing position, and its legs were not nearly long enough to be a deer's. Was it a cat?

'Hello?' Maddox whispered. 'Kitty kitty?'

Encouraged by his voice, the animal slowly, cautiously, moved toward Maddox, stumbling slightly on the uneven cushions, until Maddox could see that the creature was a furry brown dog with black button eyes like his toy animals and a pink tongue peeking between small white teeth.

'Hi, guy.' Maddox held out his hand the way his mommy had taught him, so the dog could sniff him, so the dog wouldn't feel threatened.

The dog sniffed Maddox. Its dark eyes raised expectantly to meet Maddox's eyes, and its tail wagged hopefully.

'Who are you?' Maddox asked. 'Are you lost?'

The dog dropped to its belly and crept closer to Maddox, still wagging its tail. Maddox reached out and patted the dog's head. The dog responded by scooting even nearer, keeping his yearning black eyes on Maddox's face.

'You're a nice doggy, aren't you?' Maddox said. 'What's your name? Where's your collar?' He felt around the dog's neck but no leather or metal met his fingers.

The dog, encouraged by the touching, moved closer to Maddox and licked his fingers.

A wonderful thought suddenly appeared in Maddox's mind. Could Santa have brought him this dog for Christmas?

But Christmas wasn't for two more days. And his mom didn't want a dog.

Running his fingers over the animal, he felt its ribs. Even as a small boy, he understood that the dog hadn't had much to eat recently. This dog was lost. And hungry. Maybe this dog was hiding from a mean owner. Maddox had once seen a man kick a dog. Maybe this dog had run away. Maddox knew what it felt like to want to run away.

'Maddox!' His father's voice boomed out into the yard, making Maddox jump with surprise.

'Just a minute, boy,' Maddox whispered. He crawled out the lawn chair entrance, stuck his head up, and called, 'I'm here, Daddy, in my fort.'

'Let's build a snowman. We've got time before dinner.'

'Okay, Daddy. I'll be right there.'

Back in the fort, the dog sat very obediently, his eyes searching Maddox's face.

'You're hungry,' Maddox whispered, 'but I can't bring you into the house because Mommy wouldn't like that. I'll sneak food out after dinner, I promise. Lots of good food, okay?'

The dog wagged his tail.

Delight flashed through Maddox as he realized he had a secret friend, his own private buddy. He could have adventures with this dog!

The dog needed a name. Maddox thought of famous best friends. Frog and Toad. Well, he couldn't call a dog Frog or Toad, that would be silly. He giggled to himself and the dog caught his mood, wiggling all over and climbing into Maddox's arms, licking his chin, wagging his tail. Christopher Robin and Winnie the Pooh! Maddox fell over backward, snickering.

'Pooh!' he gurgled as the dog licked his face. 'I'll name you Pooh.' Pooh was one of Maddox's favorite words because it had two meanings, one that could make his grandmother Katya raise her eyebrows. He hugged Pooh, who was cuddling as close as he could get.

'Maddox?' His father's voice sounded again.

'Coming!' Maddox answered. He sat up and put his hands on the dog's face. 'Now listen. I have to go in. You stay here. I'll bring you some food as soon as I can, okay? You'll be nice and warm here. I'll be back pretty soon.'

Pooh cocked his head, his dark eyes deep with intelligence, as if he understood every word.

Daddy decided they should build the snowman in the front yard so people could see him. He showed Maddox how to squeeze the snow tight to pack it. Together they rolled up three balls, stacking them up before adding fallen sticks for arms. Daddy opened the

front door, calling in to ask Nicole for a carrot for the nose while Maddox looked beneath the bushes until he found two rocks for the eyes. The rocks were different sizes, so the snowman looked kind of funny but still cute.

When they stepped inside, the house seemed hot and bright. As his father helped him strip off his snow boots, mittens, coat, and hat, Maddox realized how dark it looked outside if you were inside a building, even though a pearly sheen of light lingered in the air from streetlights and moonlight falling on the snow.

'Let's wash your hands and face,' Daddy said, taking Maddox's hand and leading him to the bathroom.

Mommy was up, sitting in the living room talking to Granddad. Nicole was trotting back and forth between the kitchen and the dining room. Maddox loved washing his hands and playing with the water. He could make lines of water run one way or the other and splash pools in the sink.

'Enough,' his father said. 'You're getting your sweater wet. Come on, Maddox.'

Reluctantly, Maddox slowly turned off the faucets and dried his hands. Here came the boring part of his day, sitting at the dining room table with adults. They took so long to eat their food! He could gobble his down and be ready to play in a jiffy, but his parents

wanted him to sit there like a statue, not rocking back and forth on his chair or tapping his fingers on the table or swinging his feet or even making fart noises with his mouth. This was one of the many things he couldn't understand about adults.

The food smelled good, though. His mommy insisted he eat some of the yucky lettuce salad, and he forced himself to swallow a few bites of the cranberry sauce, but the dark meat on his plate that his mommy said was duck made him cringe. Maddox preferred meat in tiny ground pieces, not hunks. Fortunately, the pumpkin lasagna had lots of creamy cheese, so he had two helpings of it, and all the adults praised him.

He had an awesome thought. Pooh would like the duck! He had to think of a way to smuggle it to the dog. He considered various options while the adults blabbed away, their cheeks growing rosy as they ate the warm food and drank their wine. The table was pretty with glowing candles making the silver shine. It was nice, seeing his parents having a good time with Granddad and Nicole. When Granddad got up to pour Daddy more wine, he blocked Maddox from his mother's vision for a few seconds, just enough time for Maddox to sneak a chunk of duck into his trouser pocket. Then he got the cool idea of putting the meat in his mouth,

pretending to chew, then wiping his mouth with his napkin and spitting the meat into the napkin. Pretty soon he had a nice glob of meat to take to Pooh.

Maddox was proud. This must be how it felt to be a superhero.

Chapter Seventeen

After dinner, everyone but Kennedy helped Nicole carry the plates, glasses, and platters into the kitchen. Even Maddox willingly skipped back and forth with his utensils and napkin. Kennedy sat at the table, grounded like a blimp, listening to all the others chatter as they loaded the dishwasher and put away leftovers. How peppy they sounded. She put her elbows on the table and dropped her head in her hands.

She heard James yell, 'Maddox, where are you going?'

Maddox called back, 'I left something in my fort.'

The back door slammed.

'You need a coat!' James cautioned, noting in a

lower voice, 'That kid. Where does he get his energy?' James flicked on the back outdoor light.

The back door slammed again as Maddox returned.

'Don't go out again without a coat,' his father ordered him. 'And stamp your feet on the mudroom rug. Don't track snow through the house.'

Kennedy's father clapped his hands in the front hall. 'Okay, everyone. Time to see Christmasland!'

'What's that, Granddad?'

'You'll see. Put on your coat. We won't be leaving the car, so you don't have to bundle up too much.' Sebastian came into the dining room. 'You're coming with us, aren't you, Kabey?' Lowering his voice, he added enticingly, 'Over by Surfside Road, it looks like the North Pole. Several of the streets have houses with every kind of lighted holiday spectacle you can imagine. Santa and his reindeer and sleigh on the roof. Frosty the Snowman. Beautiful life-size crèches.'

Kennedy placed her hands on her belly. 'I'd love to go but I'm not feeling very good. I'm not sure the food agreed with me. Duck is so rich.'

'Would you like some bicarb of soda in water?'

'That would be great, Daddy, thanks.'

Her father went off to the kitchen. Kennedy hauled herself up from the table and slowly lumbered into the living room, where she collapsed on a sofa.

'Mommy, aren't you coming?' Maddox asked.

'Not tonight, sweetie.' Kennedy smoothed her son's ruffled hair. 'You go with Daddy and Granddad.'

'Nicole, too.' Maddox's eyes were shining with excitement, his cheeks rosy from his run out into the cold.

'My big boy.' Kennedy hugged him to her as well as she could. 'I love you, Mad Man.'

The others congregated in the front hall, pulling on gloves and coats while Nicole did her St Martyr of the Household bit again, bringing Kennedy a pile of magazines and tucking a blanket over her feet. Maddox was jumping up and down with antici-pation. Kennedy's father helped Nicole into her down coat. Kennedy felt childishly miffed at herself. Everyone else was giddy and good-natured. She was like a fat female Scrooge.

As soon as she saw the Grand Cherokee's lights fade into the distance, she levered herself off the sofa. Trundling up the stairs to the second floor, she headed down the long hall to the last small room, used as a storage room. Turning on the light, she was pleased to see that nothing had changed. Her grandmother's wedding gown was still zipped in a dress bag, hanging from the back of the closet. Her ice skates, skis, and rollerblades were in the closet, along with a few of her more memorable Halloween costumes and her father's high school letter jacket. One wall was lined

with shelves filled with books. Her favorite books from childhood had been pillaged to take to her home to read to Maddox. Her high school and college yearbooks were still here.

The family photo albums were here, too. Ha.

Kennedy had been a child before digital cameras hit the scene, so her parents had devotedly snapped shots, had them printed off, and slipped the best photos into handsome leather-bound albums. Getting to them now was difficult, because they lined the lowest shelves, requiring Kennedy to squat — not her easiest posture — to wrench them out of the tightly packed shelf. They were heavy, fat, and bulky. Still, she persevered, tugging them off the shelf until she had them in a pile. Then, two by two, she carried them downstairs to the living room coffee table. It was a time-consuming process. She could heft only two at a time, and she had to hold those against her body with one arm so she could grasp the stair banister with her free hand. Fourteen unwieldy albums, compressing so many years of her family's life. Huffing, puffing, gasping, wheezing, Kennedy climbed down and back up, down and back up, her lower back cramping with protest at the weight.

Finally they were gathered on the coffee table. Excellent. Nicole's prissy Christmas room with its tree,

stockings, and small wooden crèche was overwhelmed by the stack of albums. Kennedy dropped like a stone onto the sofa and caught her breath. Her back was a red hot coal of tongs squeezing her spinal cord, but she wasn't ready to rest yet. She spread as many of the albums as she could, open, photos gleaming, on the coffee table. The others she stacked on the floor in small towers of memory.

After resting, she scanned the albums until she found the one filled with pictures of herself at three, chubby and grinning from her father's arms, her mother next to them. Oh, she had been such a darling baby. Her three-year-old self sat smiling on Christmas morning, holding a baby doll in her arms. Katya wore a red and green silk robe; she was astonishingly lovely as she sat on the sofa with Sebastian's arm wrapped around her, both of them flushed with pleasure. Kennedy left that album open on the table so Nicole wouldn't fail to notice it.

Leaning back against the sofa, Kennedy allowed herself a great big helping of self-pity. Why did everything change?

A few photos of her nanny, Patty, had been included in the album. Kennedy happily remembered the woman, who smelled of sugar, flour, and baby powder. Here Kennedy was, taking her first brave steps toward Patty. Here Kennedy was with Patty at the ocean. The

reality of being so young floated just out of the grasp of Kennedy's memory, but as she opened more albums, she began to warp back into some of the scenes.

The Halloween when she was four, dressed as a princess. She'd never wanted to take those sparkling clothes off. In fact, she recalled having a fight about it with Patty because she wanted to wear the princess gown and tiara to school.

The Christmas she was ten, memorable because Patty had been let go because Kennedy was considered too old to need a nanny. The family had gone to Aruba for Christmas. Such shimmering turquoise blue water, the palm trees, the cottage that had no television set.

Changing years, changing holiday islands. Rain forests, thatched cottages without walls, hotel rooms with television sets, her mother lying on a beach lounge, eyes covered with sunglasses, turning deep brown in the sun, then dressing for dinner and dancing with Sebastian and their friends. Kennedy got to order room service and watch videos.

Katya's clothes. Swirling silks, a sleek black bikini, skin-sleek satin. Kennedy appreciated even more as an adult how beautiful Katya was and how hard she had worked in the service of that beauty. Not only the strict dieting and exercising, but the hours spent at the beauty salon, having her hair colored and styled,

having her legs and eyebrows waxed – and Katya abhorred pain as much as Kennedy. All Kennedy's friends had Brazilian waxes, but Kennedy couldn't bring herself to do it. She could hardly bear to have her legs waxed.

In all the photos, Katya's nails were perfectly shaped and painted. Discreet but expensive gems gleamed on her fingers and in her earlobes, around her neck and arms. Her mother had not been completely self-absorbed, though. She had taught Kennedy well, and Kennedy was grateful. Katya had shown Kennedy how to eat healthily if lightly, so that Kennedy didn't get caught up in the anorexia and bulimia of so many girls at her boarding school. That was a real victory.

Katya must have loved Sebastian passionately to have sacrificed the glory that was her body to the degradations of pregnancy and birth. How Katya had gotten her figure back after her pregnancy, Kennedy did not understand. She was sure she would resemble an exploded water balloon for the rest of her life.

'Mommy!' The front door burst open. Maddox ran into the room, forgetting in his excitement to be gentle with Kennedy, throwing himself onto her before even taking off his coat and mittens. 'We saw Santa on his sleigh! We saw Rudolph! We saw Charlie Brown,

and Snoopy on his doghouse! One house had lights ALL over!'

James stalked into the room. 'Hey, kid, remember to be careful with Mommy and the baby.'

Kennedy kissed Maddox's forehead. 'Did Rudolph have a red nose?'

'He did, Mommy!'

Squirming slightly to shift her son's weight, Kennedy asked, 'Was there a snowman?'

'Yeah! One house had a whole snow family!' In his excitement, he kneed Kennedy in the belly.

Kennedy couldn't help going 'Oof!'

James noticed. Swinging his son up in his arms, he said, 'Let's take your coat off, Maddox. It's time to calm down now and get ready for bed.'

Kennedy sensed her husband's gaze resting on her, giving her a moment to offer to help put their son to bed, to ask about the outing, to send him a look of gratitude. She ignored him, staring intently at the album. She took care of Maddox ninety-nine percent of the time. It was James's turn. Besides, she had a scheme to put into action.

Sebastian and Nicole entered the living room, bringing a rush of fresh cold air with them. Kennedy shivered.

'How are you, Kabey?' her father asked.

'All right.'

119

'Maybe tomorrow night you'll feel like driving over to see the lights,' Nicole suggested. 'They're amazing—'

Sebastian interrupted. 'Kennedy, what's all this? Good Lord, you didn't haul all these albums down the stairs by yourself, did you?'

Elated by her father's concern, Kennedy ducked her head and peered up at her father from beneath her eyelashes. 'I wanted to look at them. I wanted to remember all the wonderful times our family had during the holidays.'

'But honey, you could have hurt yourself. You should have waited for us to come home and bring them down.'

Nicole knelt by the coffee table, focusing on the album Kennedy had left open where Katya was at her most young and staggeringly gorgeous.

'Katya is such a true beauty,' Nicole said, touching the photo with her forefinger. 'But you know, Sebastian, I think your daughter is even more beautiful.'

What? Kennedy wanted to totally *throw up*. Was Nicole demented? Was she some kind of frontal lobe victim? No, she was a genius at pretense, she wasn't going to let Kennedy get to her, she was acting like someone without a stick of jealousy, all gooiness.

'Nicole's right,' Sebastian said. 'You are more lovely than your mother, Kennedy.'

Kennedy's lower lip trembled. 'Thanks, Daddy.'

Bracing herself, she began the awkward effort of elevating her bulging body from the sofa. 'I think I'll go to bed now. I did get tired, carrying all those albums. But they cheered me up, so it was worth it.'

Chapter Eighteen

Christmas Eve day, a storm was predicted by the Weather Channel, with rising winds toward evening, so after breakfast Nicole and Sebastian headed off to the grocery store. They needed to stock the house with perishables and last-minute goodies and pick up the fresh, twenty-one-pound turkey. Tonight Nicole was serving beef Wellington with lots of veggies and a pumpkin pie for dessert.

First Nicole and Sebastian dropped James and Maddox at the wharves to watch the ferries come home. The wind-driven current was so strong it slammed the great behemoth car ferry the *Eagle* into the side of the dock, crashing like thunder. Fishing boats were tied up to the piers, bobbing like bathtub toys in the churning harbor.

At Stop & Shop, Nicole and Sebastian loaded up the cart, lugging armfuls of bags out to the car.

'We bought fresh cream?' Nicole wondered aloud as they left the parking lot.

'We did. I checked it off the list. We're set,' Sebastian assured her. 'We have enough food to feed us for the next week.'

'I hope so. If the storm is as bad as they say, the boats may not be able to make it over with fresh supplies for days.'

Sebastian reached over and held her hand. 'The storm might miss us and blow out to sea. If it does hit, we're in a house that's stood for over a hundred years. Twenty-five years ago, we had trouble with power going out, but the electric company installed an underwater cable, so we'll be just fine.'

'Oh, heavens, I hadn't even thought about losing electricity.'

'You worry too much,' Sebastian said.

You don't have five people to feed three meals a day, Nicole wanted to remind him, but she didn't want to seem to be complaining. And she wasn't. She loved cooking. She loved the holiday season. She adored Maddox, liked James just fine . . . and she was proud of the way she was keeping her cool with Kennedy. She was unaccountably nervous, though, she was on edge, as if her woman's intuition was warning her of trouble ahead. No

doubt this was caused by the falling barometer, the increasing wind, and the frenzied ions or protons or whatever was invisibly frothing in the air.

They picked up a windblown James and Maddox and returned home. James helped Sebastian and Nicole carry in the multitude of bags.

Maddox ran straight to his mother. Kennedy was sitting in a chair by the fire in the living room.

'It was awesome, Mommy!' Maddox squealed, throwing himself into her lap.

'Ouch.' Kennedy recoiled as her son literally knocked the breath out of her. Seeing Maddox's face flicker with anxiety, she reached out and pulled him up onto her knees, hugging him tightly. 'I'm okay, sweetie. Now tell me all about the ocean. How high were the waves?'

'This high!' Maddox proudly raised his arm as far as it would go above his head.

'Wow.' Kennedy widened her eyes in appreciative astonishment. 'I hope you held Daddy's hand.'

'I did, Mommy, I did. And the big ferry boat went *crash* into the—' He frowned, unsure of the right word.

'The dock?' Kennedy suggested, lovingly smoothing her son's hair.

'Yeah! And—' Maddox wiggled with excitement, describing the adventure.

Nicole hummed as she stripped off her coat and unpacked the groceries. It was good to see Kennedy happy. She put on Christmas music in her kitchen, and the sparkling arms of her holiday sweater brightened her mood as she worked. This was her favorite sweater, with Santa on his sleigh in the front, the reindeer prancing around the side so that Rudolph with his cherry-red nose glittered on her back.

She prepared an easy lunch of tomato soup and grilled cheese sandwiches (on whole wheat bread, of course).

Maddox was still overexcited from his outing, almost jumping up and down in his chair.

'Sit still, Maddox,' Kennedy told her son. 'You'll spill your soup.' She looked tired. 'James, would you help him with the soup? It's so difficult for a four-year-old to eat.'

Nicole's heart cringed. 'Tell you what.' Quickly she rose from the table, easing Maddox's bowl away from him. 'I'll pour your soup into a mug, and then you can drink it.'

'Good idea,' James affirmed.

Kennedy was silent as Nicole got down a Christmas mug.

'The snow's accumulating,' Sebastian reported, turning the conversation to the view out the windows. 'We don't usually have snow this soon,' he explained

to James. 'Thirty miles out at sea, we're caught in the Gulf Stream, which keeps us warmer than the mainland.'

'It's ideal for Christmas.' Nicole set the mug in front of Maddox and resumed her seat. 'It makes everything so pretty.'

Kennedy rolled her eyes and sighed.

James, with an impatient thinning of his mouth, shot his wife a glance. 'Are you okay, Kennedy?'

'As a matter of fact, no,' Kennedy puffed. 'I think I'm coming down with some kind of flu. Or something I ate last night didn't agree with me.'

Sebastian leaned forward, concerned. 'Perhaps you should go back to bed.'

'It's Christmas Eve,' Kennedy protested. 'I don't want to lie in bed today.'

Nicole took a deep breath. She kept her mouth shut. Let the men sort Kennedy out, she decided. Nothing Nicole could do or say would help.

'Want to read to Maddox by the fire?' Sebastian suggested.

'Good idea,' James quickly agreed. 'He's had a good outing this morning—'

James's words were interrupted by a loud pounding at the front door.

Nicole jumped up. 'I'll get it. It might be presents from someone!' Hurrying optimistically down the hall,

she threw open the front door, letting in a blast of cold air and snow.

A woman in a mink coat and hat strode past Nicole, slamming the door behind her, shaking flakes off her shoulders, stamping her leather high-heeled boots on the rug. She acted as if she were entering her own house.

Well, in a way, she was.

Nicole had never fainted but at this moment she had an excellent sense of how it might feel.

'Katya?' She had seen photos of Katya before, but she'd never laid eyes on the woman in person, in her glorious Technicolor glamour.

'Damn, it's wicked out there,' Katya said. She stripped her leather gloves off her long hands and dropped them on the front hall table. 'You've moved the front hall chair,' she said to Nicole. 'Where am I going to sit down to take off my boots?'

Nicole was speechless.

'Mommy?' Kennedy hurried into the hall, eyes wide. 'Mommy! What are you doing here?'

'Oh, Kennedy.' Katya turned her back on Nicole and held her arms out to her daughter. 'Sweetie, thank heavens.' She hugged Kennedy tightly.

Sebastian entered the hall, a perplexed expression on his face. 'Katya?'

'Sebby.' Reaching out, Katya put her hand on her ex-husband's chest. 'I apologize for arriving like this,

but I just *had* to be here with my family. Alonzo and I had a terrible fight.' Katya's head drooped elegantly, like a tulip. 'We're finished.'

Kennedy's face lit up like a beacon. 'You and Alonzo broke up?' Her eyes fluttered back and forth between her father and mother.

Nicole allowed herself to tilt backward slightly, in order to be supported by the wall. She forced herself to breathe.

Sebastian stepped away from his ex-wife's touch. 'Why did you come here?' he asked. His voice was cool, and for that Nicole was grateful.

Katya simpered. 'I've spent practically every Christmas of my life in this house. Kennedy's here. My grandson is here. Where else could I turn for comfort?'

'You did the absolutely right thing, Mommy,' Kennedy assured her mother.

Sebastian's face darkened. 'Don't you think you're being rather insensitive?' he demanded.

Katya gazed innocently, widening her crystal-blue eyes. 'What do you mean?'

Nicole's heart fluttered so rapidly she was afraid she was going to hyperventilate, pass out, and slide down the wall to the floor.

In three strides, Sebastian was next to Nicole. He put his arms around her shoulders. 'This is Nicole's house now, not yours.'

'Daddy!' Kennedy cried.

'Oh, surely—' Katya began to object.

'Grandmama!' Maddox ran into the hall and stared up at Katya, mouth open in wonder.

'Katya,' James said, following his son. 'What are you doing here?'

'James, darling. And precious Maddox, my own grandson.' Katya knelt to embrace the boy. 'Grandmama's here to spend Christmas with you, Maddox. Isn't that wonderful?'

Chapter Nineteen

Her mother was here! Kennedy was breathless with amazement, and her heart seemed to be expanding alarmingly as emotions jostled within her.

Rapture at seeing her mother, actually here in this house.

Dismay at having her mother see her, Kennedy, who had allowed herself to relax. She hadn't put on her makeup yet, and it was already after lunch. She'd been lying down in front of the fire and hadn't brushed her hair since – well, she couldn't remember. Compared to Katya in her camel-hair trousers and cashmere sweater, her heavy gold necklace and earrings, Kennedy was absolutely frumpy in her red maternity tent.

Hope at the possibility of her parents getting back

together, because here they both were in the same house, and Alonzo was in the past!

Despair at seeing her father move away from Katya to put his arm around Nicole.

'I need to sit down,' she murmured.

'Of course you do, sweetheart.' Katya handed her mink to James. Over her shoulder, she said to Sebastian, 'My suitcase is on the front stoop. Could you bring it in, please?' With an arm around her daughter, she cooed, 'Let's go into the living room and get you comfy.'

They settled on the sofa. Kennedy angled her bulk to allow herself to study her mother's face. Katya's eyes were slightly pink and swollen. Obviously she had been crying, something she seldom allowed herself to do, and Kennedy's heart broke for her mother.

'Are you okay, Mommy?'

Katya bristled. 'Don't I look okay?'

'Of course. You're as beautiful as always. But you must be sad without Alonzo.'

Katya stared down at her hands. 'Devastated.' A shadow passed over her face.

In that moment, Kennedy saw the slight sag of flesh around her mother's lovely jawline and the pouch beneath her eyes that had not been quite disguised by concealer.

'Oh, Mommy.'

Katya stiffened at the compassion in Kennedy's voice. 'It happened only last night. I haven't slept. I know I look dreadful, but I'm extremely tired. Shattered, really, with the packing and the trip. It was a horrendous flight, very bumpy, the wind *shook* the plane. What I'd *adore* is a hot bath and a good nap.'

'Of course,' Kennedy began, just as her father walked into the room. Kennedy's spirits lifted. 'Daddy, Mommy wants—'

'Katya.' Sebastian's voice was terse. He remained standing. 'You've got to realize how inappropriate it is for you to be here.'

'Daddy!' Kennedy burst out.

'I'm sorry if you and Alonzo broke it off, but the fact is that is *your* matter to deal with, not mine. You and I were divorced years ago. You're a grown woman, you have plenty of financial resources – I've seen to that. You need to make other plans.'

Katya slanted her head submissively. Fluttering her lashes, she pleaded, 'I have no place else to go.'

'You must have friends on the mainland,' Sebastian pointed out.

Katya shrugged. 'No one I could go to for the holiday.'

'Fine. Then a hotel. You've always been fond of first-class hotels.'

Kennedy's mood rose at this sign of her father remembering what her mother preferred.

'A hotel? On Christmas?'

'We've often stayed in hotels on Christmas,' Sebastian reminded her as he stalked to the fire, stirred it with the poker, then shot Katya a sober stare. 'I suggest you try to get a room at the Ritz or the Taj in Boston.'

Katya lifted her shoulder coyly to her cheek. 'I'm not sure I can leave the island. With this storm . . .'

Sebastian's face darkened with annoyance. Straightening, he decreed, 'Then go to one of the hotels on Nantucket. The Jared Coffin House.'

'The expense—' Katya started to object.

'I'll pay for it.' Sebastian folded his arms over his chest, a sign that he was not going to yield.

Katya tossed her lovely blond hair. 'Fine. But Sebastian, be kind. I'm so awfully tired. I was just telling Kennedy that I didn't sleep a wink last night. Couldn't I take a brief lie-down here before I go back out into the storm?'

'Please, Daddy,' Kennedy begged. 'Mommy can rest on my bed, and while she rests, I'll phone the Nantucket hotels and see who has a room.'

Sebastian did not look pleased.

'Sebby.' Katya stood up, stepping close to her ex-husband, putting her hand on his arm. 'I'm sorry

about all of this. I know I've made so many many terrible mistakes. If I could only turn back the clock . . .'

Kennedy watched her mother and father with hope springing up in her heart.

'You can't turn back time, Katya.' Sebastian didn't sound angry or bitter or punitive, but adamant. Quietly, he walked away from her to the door into the front hall. 'And I'm glad about that. Now please have some consideration and take yourself to a hotel.'

Her father left the room.

Katya turned away so that Kennedy couldn't see her face. Kennedy's stomach cramped with regret and despair. It was not going to happen. Her parents were never going to get back together. That damned Nicole had bewitched her father, although how anyone so plain could bewitch anyone was past Kennedy's comprehension.

She heard Nicole in the kitchen, chatting quietly with James and Maddox. 'Well, Maddox,' Nicole said, 'if you eat every bite of your sandwich, you may have a candy cane, but only if your daddy says so.'

Who was Nicole to control what Kennedy's child ate? Annoyance propelled Kennedy ungracefully off the sofa.

'Mommy. Let me take you to my room so you can rest.'

In the hall, Katya started to climb the stairs.

'No, wait. We're in the birthing room behind the kitchen,' Kennedy informed her mother. 'So I don't have to climb the stairs all the time.'

'Good idea,' Katya replied. She hesitated, understandably reluctant to enter the kitchen.

Kennedy took her mother's hand and pulled her along. Nicole was at the sink, rinsing dishes before stacking them in the dishwasher. James was covering a platter of fresh veggie strips with cling wrap. Maddox sat on a chair, swinging his legs, sucking a candy cane.

'Mommy's going to take a brief nap,' Kennedy proclaimed, her tone of voice leaving no room for discussion.

'I'm going to take a nap, too, Grandmama,' Maddox told her.

Katya crouched down to kiss her grandson. 'Have a good sleep, my angel. I'll see you later.' Rising, she followed Kennedy into the birthing room.

'The bathroom's through here,' Kennedy began, then stopped, blushing. 'Of course you know that.'

Katya looked around the room. 'So Nicole changed the den into a bedroom.' With a sigh, she sat down on the wide bed that, Kennedy realized with a blip of relief, she had actually made this morning. Unzipping her boots, Katya kicked them off, raised her shapely legs onto the bed, and reclined onto a pillow. 'Oh, my. This feels divine.'

Kennedy unfolded a patchwork quilt and spread it over Katya. She kissed her mother's forehead. 'Have a good rest.'

'Thank you, dear.' Katya closed her eyes.

Kennedy left the room, quietly shutting the door, thinking how odd it felt to do something so maternal to her own mother.

Chapter Twenty

The boy's fort was better than nothing, but the temperature was falling while the wind rose. It was late afternoon and the boy who called him Pooh hadn't brought him anything to eat since last night when he brought out that piece of excellent meat.

He worried the boy had forgotten him. The light that came with morning was already fading. This was good for when Snix needed to sneak out of his fort and scurry over behind a bush to pee. It made him less visible to the people inside the brightly lighted house. But it was bad for finding food. So was the snow pelting down everywhere. Already it was piled so high that Snix had trouble lifting his short legs in and out of it. Once or twice he got stuck, which

made him even colder. He jumped his way back into the fort, his coat covered with flakes.

He licked the icy white off his legs and shoulders and rolled on the cushions. He tried nosing a cushion up against another one to make a notch where he could wriggle down into for warmth. It didn't work very well. The wind was so strong it rattled the lawn chairs and lifted the edges of the cardboard and blankets.

He couldn't understand why the boy hadn't come back. Perhaps this was the way humans were, hugging and feeding you one day, completely forgetting you the next.

Or maybe it was that Snix was unlovable. He wasn't much to look at, he knew. He was too small to guard a house. He was too small even to make it through the increasing piles of snow to search for food. No one needed a dog like him.

His stomach growled as hunger clawed at it. He whimpered pathetically.

Wait! He heard a noise. The back door was opening. He crawled to the edge of the lawn chair tunnel and peeked out between the slats.

It wasn't the boy. Snix's heart sank.

But it was a woman carrying a heavy clear bag of garbage, and even through the blowing snow Snix could smell the layers of cooked and raw food.

These people had a heavy plastic garbage can with a tight-fitting lid that clamped shut so decidedly that Snix had never been able to open it.

But he'd never been this desperate before. He would wait until the woman went back inside, then attack the garbage can with all his might.

Chapter Twenty-one

At preschool, everyone talked about Christmas as full of excitement, presents, good food, and fun. But Christmas was tomorrow and everyone in the house was grumpy. Maddox could *feel* the heaviness. He knew he was only a kid, he couldn't understand everything, but he knew when people bustled or whistled or sang, and right now the house was silent except for the sound of Nicole clashing pots and pans in the kitchen.

That was wrong. Nicole always fluttered around in the kitchen like a butterfly, humming to herself. Now her expression was grim. Grandmama had disappeared into the bedroom. Mommy and Daddy were in the living room, talking in low voices. Granddad sat in the kitchen nook, phoning hotels.

The windows rattled, battered by the storm. *Pooh!*, Maddox thought. Maddox hadn't been able to get outside to take him food since yesterday, because he always had a grown-up taking him here and there. The poor dog must be cold and hungry.

This might be the perfect time to sneak outside with some food. Maddox had eaten all of his grilled cheese sandwich, but the grown-ups hadn't. Nicole was piling the crusts into the trash bag now, where they joined bits of bacon, eggs, toast, and other breakfast goodies that had been left over from this morning. It would be a feast for his puppy pal!

How could he steal the bag away from Nicole? Already it looked too heavy for Maddox to carry it, but he could drag it, but not in front of the grownups . . . While he deliberated, Nicole swiftly twisted and tied the opening, hefted it up, and headed to the mudroom and the back door.

Disappointment flooded Maddox. He knew he wasn't strong enough to unclamp the garbage cans. But he had to be inventive, he had to be strong, he had to feed Pooh. Quickly scanning the kitchen, he discovered a box of Cheerios left on the counter. Okay, maybe dogs didn't eat Cheerios, but it was better than nothing.

Like a spy, Maddox slipped out to the mudroom, pulled on his boots, then dove beneath the bench

where people sat to take off their boots or put them on. The door opened, snow gusted in on an invisible carpet of cold air, and Nicole's feet strode past, stamping snow onto the floor. She went into the kitchen.

Maddox sneaked out from under the bench. Reaching up, he turned the knob and pulled the back door open. Sliding through the smallest possible opening, he stepped out onto the back porch and pulled the door shut tight.

Light from the kitchen fell onto the porch and backyard. From here he could see how the wind buffeted the fort, clattering the cardboard against the wood and making the edges of the blankets lift and drop. Still, it stood. So Pooh was warm inside.

Maddox hurried down the steps toward the fort. Wind spun through his hair and dotted his face with snowflakes, but he was warm enough in the wool Christmas sweater Nicole had knit especially for him.

Kneeling down, he crawled through the lawn chair entrance into the fort.

'Pooh!' he called. 'I'm here. I'm here, Pooh. I've brought you something to eat.'

Pooh wasn't there.

Chapter Twenty-two

As Nicole carried out the garbage, she wondered why Sebastian was making phone calls on his ex-wife's behalf. This garbage bag was heavy, but Sebastian was too busy on the phone, helping Princess Katya. For heaven's sake, couldn't James or Kennedy or Katya herself make the calls? Were Katya's filed, French-tipped fingernails too delicate to punch numbers into a phone?

Bah, humbug, Nicole thought as she tromped up the back steps. All her visions of a lollipop Noel had fled before the nightmare of gorgeous, vulnerable Katya arriving to take over the house and the holiday.

Back in the house, she saw James secluded in the

living room whispering with Kennedy. Sebastian was in the kitchen, grim-faced.

'Most of the hotels and B&Bs are closed for the season. The few that are open are booked. No rooms available.' Seeing Nicole's frustration, he tried to lighten the moment. 'No room at the inn.'

Nicole was aware that her hair had been stirred by the wind into all kinds of crazy. She had tried to ignore the fact that her middle-aged bottom had grown bigger and rounder as she'd spent the month cooking delicacies for the holiday, but with Katya here, so slim and toned, Nicole admitted to herself that she looked like a peasant compared to a queen. No, not a peasant, a servant. The mild, self-effacing worker bee who cooked the meals, did the dishes, made the beds, and dusted and cleaned so the family, Sebastian's family, could flutter through life like the aristocrats Katya assumed they were.

Nicole lifted her hand to smooth down her hair. 'Right now, at this particular moment, I'm not in the mood to be benevolent.'

Sebastian swayed back, surprised. Nicole seldom spoke in this way. He apologized, 'I'm sorry I didn't carry out the garbage. I know the bag was heavy.'

'I'm bushed,' Nicole told him, and it was true. She was at the end of her rope, which allowed all sorts of demonic phrases to pepper her mind, filling her with dark thoughts.

I'll leave. I'll go to Jilly's and let you have your perfect wife and family all back together again. Those words were on the tip of her tongue, but she knew they weren't rational, she was simply overemotional and overwhelmed. Sebastian had not done anything to make her doubt his love for her. He had stepped away when Katya tried to paw him. He had put his arm around Nicole. She had to tamp down her temper.

'I'm going upstairs to lie down,' Nicole said. 'I need a rest.'

Her heart lightened when Sebastian said, 'I'll come with you.'

They lay side by side on their backs on the bed. Nicole stared at the ceiling.

Sebastian reached for Nicole's hand. 'I'm sorry Katya showed up like this. She's never been considerate of other people.'

'She wants you back,' Nicole stated bluntly.

Sebastian rolled over and put an arm around Nicole, pulling her close to him. 'I am married to you. I am in love with you.' He nibbled her ear. 'You and I are a team, Nicole. In a couple of days, everyone else will be gone, and you and I will have our house and our lives back to ourselves.'

'Yes, but when Kennedy has her baby, you and Katya and James will be with her and I'll be exiled.'

Sebastian took a deep breath. 'Exiled is putting it a bit strong.'

Nicole didn't speak.

'What can I do?' Sebastian asked. 'It's what my daughter requested. And Katya and I are the biological grandparents.' After a moment, he continued, 'Give Kennedy a break. She's a good person, deep down. She's not thinking clearly. I think she's pretty over-whelmed by pregnancy hormones.'

Nicole turned on her side, away from Sebastian. Truly, she was fed up with shopping, cooking, cleaning, deco-rating, not to mention pretending that Kennedy's little act with the photo albums hadn't wounded her. And the worst was yet to come. If Katya stayed for Christmas, how would that work? Everyone was aligned to Kennedy except Nicole, who was left out. And what about the cooking and cleaning up? If Katya didn't help, Nicole would feel like her maid. If Katya *did* help, Nicole would be painfully aware that Katya had cooked in the kitchen for years.

Tears were pressing against her chest and her eyes. 'I w-wanted this to be a wonderful Christmas,' she managed to stutter.

'What can I do to help?' Sebastian repeated. 'There must be something.'

Why couldn't Sebastian just *know*? Nicole struggled for an answer. 'Be with me,' she told him. 'Don't let

Katya touch you. Don't respond to her flirting. Make it clear that this is *our* house now, your house and mine.'

Sebastian cuddled her against him. 'I'll do that. And remember, Nicole, Katya and I were estranged even before the divorce. She pretty much lived in the Boston house while I preferred to live here. I was relieved when she ran off with Alonzo – but I've told you all this before.'

Reassured by the warmth of his arms and his words, Nicole agreed, 'Okay. I can do this. If you're by my side.'

'Don't worry, I'm right here.' Sebastian hugged her tightly.

Yet Nicole knew that, for her, Christmas was ruined.

Chapter Twenty-three

Kennedy could not get comfortable on the living room sofa. She had eaten too much of Nicole's amazingly delicious food. Rubbing her hands over her swollen belly, she closed her eyes and tried to relax, but thoughts of her mother stirred through her emotions. As much as Kennedy had hated it when her mother divorced her father, she had been glad for Katya whenever Katya was with Alonzo, because this new love had made Katya glitter in ways Kennedy had never seen before. Katya had acted silly, hugging and smooching Kennedy with a carefree, spontaneous enthusiasm that was entirely new.

Now Alonzo and Katya were over. Kennedy could tell her mother was hurting more than she let others

see. The fact that Katya wanted to take a nap? *Whoa.* Katya had never taken naps before.

James was outside, shoveling the walk and the drive. The sound of the blade hitting the bricks made Kennedy grit her teeth. Couldn't he wait?

If only Nicole would just *leave.* Then Kennedy's father wouldn't have to behave so dutifully to his new wife. Sebastian would be free to gaze upon Katya with clear eyes, he would see that they belonged together, he would take her in his arms, and everyone in the house would belong.

Chapter Twenty-four

'Pooh!' Maddox struggled through the backyard, following the bumpy path through the snow toward the garage. 'Pooh! Where are you?'

The snow reached the top of his boots. The wind pushed at him, and snow swirled up his nose. Fear burned his heart, shame sliced his belly. He should have brought the puppy some food this morning. If Pooh had run away because he thought Maddox had abandoned him . . . Maddox sobbed aloud. The sound flew away in the storm.

It wasn't quite dark yet. Lights from the house fell over the yard, and as Maddox went around the side of the garage, his heart exploded with gladness. There he was! The little terrier was standing on his hind legs,

trying to push over the heavy garbage container, which rocked but did not fall.

'Pooh!'

The dog turned, saw Maddox, and, yelping jubilantly, bounded through the few feet between them, throwing himself at Maddox with delirium. Maddox put his arms around the animal. Pooh was shivering. Pooh whined with ecstasy, licking Maddox's face with an icy tongue.

'You're going inside with me,' Maddox told the animal.

He tried to pick Pooh up in his arms, and he did manage it, but the dog's weight made Maddox almost fall over backward. Heroically, Maddox toiled forward, one step at a time, through the mountains of white. The dog rested his head on Maddox's shoulder. It was the most wonderful feeling. Keeping to the jagged path he had broken through on his way out, he managed to labor his way right up to the steps to the back porch. Here, he collapsed, out of breath.

'Pooh,' he gasped, setting the dog down next to him.

Pooh squeezed as close to Maddox as he could. They were both quaking with cold.

Maddox stood up. His snowboots were warm, but they were heavy. He'd be glad to get them off. Resolutely, he climbed the wooden steps.

'Come on, Pooh,' he called. The dog leapt up the steps, right alongside Maddox.

Maddox reached way up to turn the doorknob. He shoved the door open. Warmth flooded out from the mudroom.

'Come on, Pooh,' he called again.

Pooh didn't hesitate. He bounced across the porch and into the house. Maddox pulled the door shut. In the bright light, he saw how each individual hair on Pooh's body was crusted with snow. It frosted poor Pooh's nose and the tips of his ears. Maddox seized his own navy blue coat with the red plaid lining and wrapped it over the dog, holding him tightly.

'Maddox!' Suddenly Grandmama Katya loomed in the doorway, looking cross and even kind of mean. 'What is *that*?'

Chapter Twenty-five

S nix nestled his head on the boy's shoulder, savoring this surprising moment of belonging. He was wanted. He was *chosen*. He was very nearly warm.

And he'd bet the little boy would feed him any minute now. His stomach rumbled hungrily. He hoped the boy could feel it.

The boy's arms tightened around Snix when the thin blond woman came into the mudroom. Snix felt him tense up. He could smell the woman's scent, much like cat pee, and the boy's anxiety. Snix stayed still, sensing it was a good time to be invisible.

The woman kept saying *Maddox*. Maddox must be the boy's name. Good to know.

'Santa brought him to me,' Maddox told the woman.

She laughed, but the sound wasn't lighthearted. 'Maddox, Christmas isn't until tomorrow, *darling*. Besides, dogs aren't allowed in the house.'

Maddox's arms were trembling from supporting Snix's weight. Squatting down, he put Snix on the floor. He removed his coat from Snix's body. 'He's just a *little* dog,' Maddox pointed out.

Snix tried to squeeze himself small. He lay down on the floor – the soft rag rug felt good against his belly – and put his head between his paws.

'I don't care what size the animal is. Dogs are not allowed in this house.'

'Excuse me?' Another woman entered the mudroom. This one didn't smell like cat pee. She smelled wonderful. She smelled like food. 'Oh, Maddox, who is this?'

Food Woman knelt next to Snix. Snix lifted his head hopefully. Food Woman slowly reached out to let Snix smell her hand, a true courtesy, then gently scratched him behind his ears.

'Hello, cutie-pie. What's your name?'

In reply, Snix licked her wrist, perhaps a bit too enthusiastically, but it was ringed with the slight aroma of melted cheese.

'Pooh,' Maddox told Food Woman. 'I've named him Pooh.'

'Well, Pooh, you appear just a tad bedraggled. I'll

bet you'd like something to eat. Perhaps a nice bowl of warm milk and a bit of—'

'Don't tell me you intend to feed that creature!' Blond Woman was indignant. 'If you do that, you'll never get rid of him.'

'Santa brought him!' Maddox protested, getting to his feet. 'He did, Nicole!'

'Dogs are not allowed in this house,' Blond Woman said, her voice as cold as the wind outside.

Food Woman spoke, her voice low, vibrating with indignation. 'May I remind you, you do not make the rules here. This is not your house any longer.'

'Mommy!' shouted Maddox as another woman squeezed her bulk into the room. She was young and pretty and hugely fat.

'What's wrong? Maddox, what have you done?'

'Mommy.' Maddox babbled, suddenly crouching over Snix. 'Santa left me this dog. I want to keep him. His name is Pooh. He won't eat much.'

Actually . . . Snix thought, almost dizzy with hunger and the enticing bouquet of beef, cheese, and oatmeal . . .

His thoughts were interrupted. 'I've told you, Maddox, you can't have a pet. I'm sorry, but we're going to have a new baby soon.'

'But, Mommy—' Maddox argued, stamping his foot.

'MADDOX, you are being a very BAD boy!' his mother yelled.

'Then *I'll* keep him,' Food Woman announced.

'You will *not*!' Blond Woman bristled with outrage. 'An animal will ruin this house! The floors will be scratched, the furniture ripped to shreds—'

'As I said,' Food Woman replied calmly, 'this is not your house.'

Maddox's mommy turned bright red and stuck her face into Food Woman's face. 'How dare you be rude to my mother!'

'What's going on?' An older man came into the room, which made the mudroom crowded.

'Daddy!' the fat lady with the bulging tummy cried.

'Sebastian,' Blond Woman said and at the same time, Food Woman said, 'Sebastian.'

Everyone talked at once, which made it possible for Maddox to pick his coat off the floor, toss it over Snix, clutch Snix to his chest, push open the back door, and run back out into the cold.

Chapter Twenty-six

'Tell her, Daddy, *tell* her!' Kennedy threw herself into her father's arms. Tears flew from her eyes. 'Tell Nicole she is not allowed to make rules for *my* son!'

'I didn't—' Nicole began.

'Kennedy?' James came into the room. He'd finished shoveling the front walk, and snow topped his wool hat and the shoulders of his coat. 'What's going on?'

Kennedy could hardly remain standing. She was out of breath, overwhelmed by the situation, bent in half by her emotions.

Katya spoke, her voice laced with contempt for Nicole. 'Nicole thinks she can tell Kennedy how to run her life.'

'No, I do not,' Nicole disagreed, almost spitting each word.

Kennedy shuddered. 'Daddy, make her stop being mean to Mommy.'

'Kennedy.' James stepped forward and put his hand on her shoulder. 'Honey, what's gotten into you? You sound like a whining adolescent.'

Nicole folded her arms in the most *satisfied* way. Kennedy wanted to *slap* her.

'Don't you speak to my daughter that way!' Katya snapped.

'Why don't we all calm down,' Sebastian suggested. 'Let's get out of the mudroom and discuss this reasonably.'

'Discuss *what*?' James asked.

'Nicole wants to let Maddox keep the dog,' Kennedy told him.

'What dog?' James asked.

Kennedy shrieked. 'WHERE'S MADDOX?'

Silence suddenly filled the mudroom as everyone turned to stare at the place where the boy and dog had been standing. Now there was only a wet spot on the rug and a small pile of melting snow.

Sebastian strode across the empty space, yanked open the back door, and yelled out into the dark night: 'Maddox? Maddox!'

Nicole hurried to his side. Stepping out onto the

back porch, she called, 'Maddox, honey, it's okay. The dog can come in, too.'

'How dare she,' Katya muttered.

Sebastian took a flashlight from the shelf above the coat hooks and hurried out into the yard. 'Maddox? Maddox!'

'Maybe he's in his fort.' Nicole trotted down the back steps and through the snowdrifts, fell to her knees, and crawled inside the lawn chair tunnel. After a moment, she backed out. 'They're not in there.'

Kennedy's heart seemed to explode with anguish. 'What have I done?' Snatching the first coat her hand found, she pulled it over her shoulders.

As Kennedy wobbled out onto the porch and down the steps, her mother shouted, 'Kennedy! You can't go out in this weather. Not in your shape. You'll fall! Kennedy, get back in here.'

James brushed past his mother-in-law, rushed out the back door, and caught Kennedy as she reached the bottom step. 'Kennedy,' he crooned. 'It's okay.' Taking a moment, he stroked the side of her face with his hand.

James's caring touch, his concerned gaze, soothed Kennedy. For a second, in the midst of the swirling snow, the world made sense.

'James,' she sobbed. 'I was mean to Maddox. He wants to keep a puppy he found and I said he couldn't.

He said Santa brought it to him. I said . . .' She couldn't finish. She hated herself at that moment. She was the worst mother in the world. 'I told Maddox he was *bad*. On Christmas Eve. So he ran away.' She bent over double with pain.

James wrapped his arms around her tight. He was so strong. His love for her was a healing balm. 'Let's get you back inside. You need to take care of yourself. I'll go find Maddox. He can't have gone far.'

Sebastian and Nicole approached, ghostly in their snow-covered clothing.

'He's not in the yard or garage or at the front of the house,' Sebastian announced.

Kennedy choked back a sob.

Chapter Twenty-seven

Nicole had a sudden thought. 'Maybe he went up to his room. I'll check.' She raced out of the mudroom, through the front hall, and up the stairs. The door to Maddox's room was open. The room was empty.

'He's not there,' she called as she hurried back down the stairs.

'We're going to look for him,' Sebastian yelled.

'We'll find him!' James promised desperately. The two men hurried out.

The front door slammed. Nicole hesitated in the hallway, wondering whether she should join the search party, too.

Just then, to her great surprise, there came from

the mudroom an extended, anguished, guttural bellow. It was a sound Nicole knew well from her days as a nurse. She closed her eyes and took a deep breath.

Katya was helping Kennedy into the front hall.

Katya looked exasperated. 'For heaven's sake, Kennedy, enough with the melodrama. They'll find him.'

Nicole said, 'It's not melodrama, Katya. Your daughter's in labor.'

'Don't be ridiculous,' Katya countered.

Kennedy was almost crouching, hands on the wall for support.

Nicole went to the young woman. 'Let's go into the living room. It's the warmest room in the house. I'll check your contractions.'

Unable to speak, Kennedy allowed Nicole to support her as they slowly made their way into the living room. A fire flickered brightly in the fireplace, and the Christmas tree glittered in the window.

'Put your hands on the back of the chair,' Nicole told Kennedy.

Kennedy leaned on the armchair with Nicole standing behind her. Suddenly, a gush of blood-tinged water flooded from her body.

'Kennedy! What are you doing? The rug is Turkish!' Katya cried.

Nicole ignored the other woman, her hands on Kennedy's belly.

'Katya, the baby is coming. Call 911.'

'The baby isn't due for three more weeks,' Katya argued, adding, 'Maddox was ten days late.'

Kennedy was growling constantly now. Digging her hands into the back of the chair for support, she gasped, 'Mommy. *Call 911.*'

With a sniff, Katya took her cellphone out of the pocket of her cashmere skirt and punched in the numbers. She punched them in again. She looked at the phone, mystified. 'It's dead. My cell is dead.'

'Try the landline,' Nicole told her. 'In the kitchen.'

'Oooooooooh.' Kennedy's legs were shaking. 'Nicole, I think I'm having the baby.'

'Yes. I think you are, too. Don't worry, Kennedy. You'll be fine.'

Kennedy lifted her face to the ceiling, straining. A long wail tore from her body.

Katya ran in from the kitchen. 'That line's dead, too.'

'Must be the storm,' Nicole murmured, preoccupied.

'Kennedy, are you okay?' Katya's splendid forehead wrinkled in concern.

Nicole calmly informed her: 'Katya, she's having the baby. Now.'

Katya opened her mouth to object, but her daughter's moans drove the reality past her doubts. 'Dear Lord. What can we do?'

Nicole guided Katya's hands onto Kennedy's waist. 'Hold Kennedy. Support her from behind. It's good that she's standing. Gravity will help the baby come down the birth canal.'

'Where are you going?' Katya shrieked, her voice shrill with fear.

'To scrub up. I'll get some scissors, twine, and towels.'

Katya went white. 'I'm going to faint.'

'Not now you're not,' Nicole said in a tone that brooked no disagreement. She hurried from the room.

In the kitchen, she quickly, knowledgeably, gathered the things she needed. She dashed into the guest room to collect a pile of towels and pillows. She scrubbed her hands with hot water and soap, then raced back into the living room, where Kennedy was roaring in pain while Katya held her daughter up. It was impossible to guess which woman was trembling the most.

Nicole knelt behind Kennedy and lifted the skirt of her red dress, tucking it into the neck. She sliced off Kennedy's sodden maternity panties.

'Kennedy. I'm going to check how far down your baby has come.'

'I can't do this!' Kennedy howled. 'Give me something for the pain! Please!'

'Whiskey? Brandy?' Katya offered helpfully. 'I have some Advil in my travel kit.'

With expert gentleness, Nicole put one hand on Kennedy's hip, and with the other hand, she slowly explored the birth canal, delicately moving her hand up. She felt the head. As always, this first touch filled her with wonder and gratitude.

'Kennedy. Your baby's almost here.'

Kennedy screamed. 'Please! It hurts too much! I can't!'

Katya was weeping. 'Help her, Nicole. Do something.'

'Do you think you can move to the coffee table?' Nicole asked.

'Are you mad?' Katya asked. 'The coffee table isn't long enough for her to—'

'I don't want her to lie down on it. I want her to lean her arms on it. I don't think she can stand up much longer.'

Gasping, crimson-faced, Kennedy managed the few awkward steps, supported by her mother and Nicole.

Nicole swept the bronze bowl of nuts off onto the floor and tossed a pillow in its place. She helped Kennedy lower herself so that each knee was on a pillow and her arms and upper body were supported by the table. She put another pillow between Kennedy's legs.

'Oh, God!' Kennedy shrieked. 'The baby's coming! The baby's coming! I can feel him coming!'

'Kennedy, listen to me. I want you to take a deep breath. When I say, I want you to push.'

'What can *I* do?' Katya wrung her hands with worry.

'Go around to the other side of the table. Hold Kennedy's shoulders. Hold her tight when she pushes.'

Katya did as Nicole said, kneeling on the floor among the flung walnuts, putting her hands on Kennedy's shoulders.

'Now, Kennedy, *push,*' Nicole said.

Kennedy gripped her mother's arms and pushed down so fiercely her body shuddered with the effort. When she stopped, she collapsed against the pillow on the coffee table, gasping for breath, too drained to speak.

Chapter Twenty-eight

'Okay, Kennedy. Again. *Push.*'

Kennedy pushed. She felt a force helping her. Her mother was helping her, holding on to her shoulders with a strength Kennedy never knew Katya had. Nicole was helping her. Nicole was a calm blur of movement and words, a serious, capable, confident strength. Something else possessed Kennedy now, a formidable, irresistible power that filled Kennedy's body like water rushing into a vessel.

She pushed, lowing like a beast.

Pain tore through her. Something ripped inside her. She bellowed.

'Your baby's crowned,' Nicole said. 'One more push and he's here.'

Shuddering, lost to the world, surrendering to what she could not evade, Kennedy yowled and pushed. The pain was unbearable – and then it diminished. She sagged against the coffee table, broken, mute, and helpless.

Behind her, Nicole was moving rapidly. 'Come over here, Katya,' she directed. 'Give me the twine. Cut it here. Tie it here. Okay, now cut.'

'Oh, God,' Katya wept. 'Oh, God, oh, God, oh, God. Kennedy, you have a baby!'

Kennedy could only keen as she felt the placenta move through her, carrying more pain along with it.

'Kennedy, we're going to help you lie down now,' Nicole said. 'Katya, pile those pillows on the floor. Kennedy, you're going to rest against the pillows so we can put your daughter in your arms.'

Through the fog of shimmering fatigue, one word stood out, in startling, terrifying bluntness. When the ultrasound was done months ago, the technician had told them the baby was a boy.

'Something's wrong with the baby,' Kennedy sobbed.

Katya and Nicole laughed together.

'Nothing's wrong with your baby,' Nicole insisted. 'Now I'm going to help you lie down. Come on, lean on me, I can take your weight, we're going to turn a bit . . . there. More comfortable?'

Kennedy's eyes cleared as her weight was supported by the cushions behind her. She saw her mother kneeling next to her, holding a naked baby in her arms.

'Kennedy, she's a little girl.' Katya lowered the baby into Kennedy's eager arms.

The baby was magenta-pink, covered with white wax, peeping like a bird, waving its arms and legs. Kennedy checked: yes, she was absolutely a little girl. The most beautiful little girl in the world.

'Oh, my baby darling,' Kennedy cooed softly.

The baby turned her face toward Kennedy, instinctively settling into Kennedy's arms, against her breasts.

Kennedy looked up at Nicole. 'Is she healthy? Does she have everything?'

Nicole was weeping and laughing at the same time. 'She's perfect. She has everything. She doesn't even seem underweight. And she's long. Look how long her legs are. She's got her all her toes, fingernails, eyebrows – she's absolutely complete.'

'She's beautiful,' Kennedy whispered.

'She is. As soon as we can get hold of a doctor, or get over to the hospital, we'll get some antibiotic ointment to put in her eyes.' Nicole held up her hand. 'It's state law. It's done for all babies at birth, to prevent infection, but it doesn't have to be done immediately, it can wait, don't worry.'

Kennedy couldn't stop staring at the tiny creature in her arms, so strange, so unknown, so entirely, absolutely belonging to her.

'Katya,' Nicole said, 'could you please get something clean and warm for Kennedy? Something soft, that opens in the front? Perhaps a cotton robe?'

'I don't want to leave the baby,' Katya confessed with tears in her eyes.

Nicole laughed. 'She'll be here when you get back. Go to my room. My softest old robe is tossed over a chair.' Nicole bent over Kennedy. 'I want to wrap your baby in this towel for warmth, then I'll give her back to you.'

Kennedy was vaguely aware of her mother leaving the room. When Nicole lifted the baby away from her, Kennedy realized how uncomfortable she was, and how soggy the towels were beneath her bum.

'Am I okay?' she asked. She realized she was shaking.

'You're fine. Childbirth is a messy business.' As she spoke, Nicole wrapped the baby and placed her back in Kennedy's arms. 'You're trembling because you've just had a baby. It's normal.'

Katya returned with the white terry cloth robe.

'Help your daughter put it on,' Nicole said. Once again, she took the baby.

Kennedy groaned as she struggled to sit up. Her mother knelt behind her, unzipping her red dress

and pulling it up over her head. She unsnapped the maternity bra, which was wet with sweat, and swiftly patted Kennedy's neck and back with a towel before helping her slip her arms into the downy robe. Katya's delicate ministrations released memories of her long-ago childhood, when her mother had helped her dress. As her mind cleared of pain, a kind of bliss replaced it at the thought of such care, such tenderness.

'Do you think you could stand up?' Nicole asked. 'You'd be more comfortable on the sofa.'

Kennedy nodded. With her mother's help, she shoved herself into a standing position. Fluids ran down her legs. 'Sorry,' Kennedy said. 'Gross.'

Nicole chuckled. 'Natural.' With another towel, she dried Kennedy's legs.

Katya supported Kennedy as she limped toward the sofa. 'Don't fall on the nuts.'

'Now why do I find that statement humorous?' Nicole wondered aloud with a grin. She was layering the sofa with more towels and plumping up pillows, working with ease and efficiency with the baby tucked in one arm.

'I need a pad between my legs,' Kennedy said.

Nicole paused. 'I don't have any.'

'I haven't had any for some time,' Katya said.

The two women looked at each other and a

171

comradely expression of relief mixed with regret passed between them.

'Well, I certainly haven't needed any for months,' Kennedy told them.

'A towel will work,' Nicole decided.

Kennedy lowered herself onto the sofa, which took her weight like a mound of clouds. Her mother arranged the robe over her legs. Nicole laid the baby in her arms. Kennedy gazed down at the pink, serene, wondering face, a face completely radiant with trust. Someone, her mother or Nicole, tucked a warm blanket around her, and Kennedy thought what a blessing it was to have that, just that, a person who covers you with a blanket and tucks it around you with care. Right now, it seemed a good reason to be born.

Chapter Twenty-nine

Maddox ran and ran. He ran down the block and around the corner before he had to stop to catch his breath. Setting Pooh down, he huffed, 'Don't run away.'

The little dog cocked his head, wagged his tail, and scooted next to Maddox's leg.

At the other end of the street, a group of people were coming out of a restaurant, guffawing, hugging, patting one another on the shoulders. The sight and sounds encouraged Maddox, drew him toward them.

It was cold. Maddox glanced at Pooh. 'You have fur,' he reasoned. 'I don't. I'll hold you if you get cold, okay?'

Pooh wagged his tail, so Maddox took his coat off

the puppy and slipped his own arms into it. The warmth was immediate and wonderful.

'Come on, Pooh,' Maddox said, lifting his chin and setting out optimistically, kicking his way through the snow. 'Maybe we'll find some nice people with a cellphone. They can call Daddy and Mommy and then . . .'

His imagination took him no further. He would get there and see what happened next. They would be sorry, his parents, especially his mommy, who had screamed at him in the most terrible voice he had ever heard, as if she hated him, as if she had turned into one of those monsters on the games big boys played. At the memory, his eyes welled with tears. He had *not* been such a bad boy. He'd done worse things before. He'd spilled stuff and been sassy, and he wasn't good at sharing.

Maybe his mommy would be glad he had left.

Pooh slipped and slid along next to Maddox as he walked down the middle of the street. Plows and sanders had come through, so this road was clear, although snow continued to fall, turning to ice as it landed.

Still, Maddox was walking toward the center of town, which blazed with lights, providing a sort of warmth in his heart. By the time he got to the restaurant, the group of people were getting into cars and

driving away, so he kept on walking, hands in his pockets, twisting his mouth around as he pondered what to do.

The bookstore was open. He saw people moving around inside.

'Come on, Pooh,' he said, reaching way up for the handle on the door.

They stepped into a pool of summer. Merriment, chatter, and delicious warm air. Maddox stood by the door a moment, just savoring the heat, aware of his dog leaning on his ankle.

'We're closing!' someone called out.

Adults, all of them very tall, crowded and jostled to get to the counter with their last-minute purchases. One of them trod on Pooh's foot. Pooh yipped in surprise. The tall man glowered down at Maddox.

'Does that animal bite?'

'No,' Maddox began. 'We need—'

But the man turned away, moving up in line. A woman with boots like his mommy wore, with long pointed dagger-like heels, stepped near Pooh, who cowered closer to Maddox.

Dismayed, Maddox picked Pooh up in his arms, pushed the door open, and went back outside. He didn't want Pooh to get stabbed in the foot. He plodded down the street, lugging Pooh in his arms.

A sudden melancholy fell over him. By now his

daddy should be running down the street, yelling for him, calling, 'Come back, Maddox! We'll let you keep the dog!'

His stomach growled. His arms hurt. He set Pooh down on the icy sidewalk. Pooh tilted his head questioningly.

'I'm hungry, Pooh, and I'll bet you are, too.' Maddox sniffed the air. No smells lured him forward.

He didn't know where to go or what to do. He'd run away full of pride and courage and filled with a sense of adventure. Now he knew he was only a cold, hungry, helpless boy.

Chapter Thirty

His boy paused on the corner. Not the smartest thing to do, Pooh thought, because the wind howled so fiercely it almost knocked Maddox over. When they were walking, their momentum carried them forward into the wind, or the wind pushed them along, but standing made Pooh shudder with cold.

He was so hungry he wanted to whimper with misery. Yet he was so overjoyed that Maddox had taken him that his misery was offset. Mostly. His belly still rumbled and complained, as if it hadn't yet received the news of his good luck.

He peered up at the boy's face, searching for a clue to his mood. Where would they go next? The boy, although young and small, was a human, with

access to doors in many warm places. He was smart and resourceful, too. After all, he'd built that warm fort.

Pooh allowed himself a moment — since Maddox was still standing there like a lump — to puzzle over the mysterious ways of humans. He knew they couldn't be trusted; Cota Collins and her family had taught him that. He had been so sure that she loved him that he hadn't even known she could *stop* loving him. Perhaps, somehow, the fault was his.

But he believed Maddox loved him. Maddox had taken him. Maddox was with him now. And Maddox was certainly lovable, such a smart, valiant boy whose plump fingers were magnificent at scratching behind Pooh's ears.

The mystery was: Why were all those humans so terrible to each other? In the midst of this black, frightening night, they were inside a warm, bright house with the swooningly good aromas of delicious food all around them. They had a *family*, and for a moment a memory flickered in Pooh's mind, of a time when he was new, snuggling with a bunch of other squirming puppies, being licked by his mother, who looked just like him and smelled of warm milk. He remembered how his eyes opened more every day, how he wobbled around the cardboard box, learning his legs, clumsily stumbling into the other

puppies – he remembered his brothers' and sisters' sharp tiny teeth! How they had rough-and-tumbled with one another, play-growling and snapping and pouncing.

He remembered how they were released out into the yard one spring morning when the grass was fragrant and the sun fell benevolently on his back. The world surprised him, it was so enormous and bright. He would run back to his mother, to be sure she was still there, then trot back to play with his siblings.

One day, Cota came. She had picked him up, hugged him to her chest, stroked his fur, whispered lovingly into his ear.

He'd never seen his siblings or his mommy again. He'd entirely lost the trail of their odor.

Would Maddox leave him, too?

His boy's words broke into his thoughts. 'Look, Pooh. We can get warm.' Maddox marched bravely forward, slipping on the occasional icy patch, lifting his feet high over drifts that had avoided the shop-keepers' shovels.

Pooh struggled along behind, leaping, sliding, trotting, limping – ice had frozen between his toes, slicing the pads of his paws.

They progressed up the sidewalk, their way lighted by the small twinkling Christmas trees, toward the giant tree at the top of Main, the one in front of the brick

building. Even this mammoth evergreen swayed from the force of the wind.

'Here!' Maddox shouted.

Snow blew into his eyes. Pooh blinked, then saw it. In front of the wide white Methodist church, on the snow-covered front lawn, stood a funny structure: a three-sided shed golden with light. A spotlight was aimed at it, making the interior blaze, and on top of the shed was another light in the shape of a star.

Inside were people and a donkey. Pooh lifted his lip to growl a warning, but as they got nearer, he realized something was off about the other creatures. They weren't the right size. They didn't smell. Ah, they were statues. A father, a mother, a baby in a cradle, and the donkey.

But on the floor of the shed was real straw. Thick, golden straw.

Pooh felt himself lifted up into Maddox's arms. The boy shoved through the snow and into the shed. They were warmer immediately, from the spotlight.

'We'll stay here,' Maddox told Pooh. The boy wriggled down at the back of the shed, holding Pooh close to his stomach, and used his hand to rake straw over their legs and torsos.

Warmer and warmer. The wind buffeted the sides of the shed, but it stood firm.

'We'll be safe here,' Maddox assured Pooh.

Pooh yipped once, lightly, in agreement. He arched his head so he could lick Maddox's hands, which were red with cold.

'We'll rest and keep warm while I think what to do next,' Maddox decided.

Pooh snuggled as close to the boy as he could. The wonderful warmth made him drowsy. But the hunger cramping his belly kept him awake.

Chapter Thirty-one

The living room was toasty. Nicole added logs to the fire and stirred it with the poker. The Christmas tree lights threw off a bit of heat, and of course the furnace was on.

Kennedy and her baby girl were ensconced on the sofa, covered and wrapped with blankets. Katya was performing the unthinkable: down on her hands and knees, she crawled around the floor, picking up walnuts and replacing them in the bronze bowl.

Nicole gathered up the pile of bloodstained towels. 'I'll get these into the washing machine.'

'Oh, thank you, Nicole,' Kennedy said. 'I don't want Maddox to be frightened when he comes in and sees so much blood.'

Katya frowned. 'The carpet is still stained. Plus, it reeks.' Suddenly, her legs buckled and she sat down, hard, on the floor. Her face was white. Her eyes were wide, her pupils dilated.

'Mommy?' Kennedy asked. 'Are you okay?'

Katya said, 'You had a baby.' Tilting her face up toward Nicole, she gasped, 'My God. What would we have done if you hadn't been here? Nicole, how can I ever thank you? I'm so grateful.' She raised her hands to her face. Her shoulders shook. She made a noise that in any other woman would be considered blubbering.

Nicole bent over and wrapped her arms around Katya. 'You're in shock. Let's get you in a chair. Come on, right here, where you can see Kennedy and the baby. You would have been fine without me,' she assured Katya. 'It's all very dramatic, isn't it?' She helped Katya stand on her shaking legs and stagger into a chair.

'Thank you, Nicole.' Katya gripped Nicole's arm. 'Truly. Thank you. I am full of admiration.'

'You're welcome. I'm glad to be part of it all.' She could tell that this was getting to be a bit more senti-mental than Katya could easily deal with. 'I'll be right back.'

She left the room, lugging the heavy soggy towels. Even after a washing, they would be pretty much shot for normal use. She'd keep them in the mudroom for

183

people to wipe off their shoes. She dumped them into the washing machine, added detergent, and turned the dial.

Then she leaned against the quietly humming machine, relaxed, and prayed. She prayed with gratitude for this new healthy baby, for Kennedy's quick and relatively painless labor and birthing, and she sent selfish words of thankfulness that everything had gone so well with Nicole at the receiving end. If anything had gone wrong, and things could have, Nicole would have been blamed. She would have blamed herself. She was always filled with both anticipation and anxiety when a mother gave birth, but this had been an extraordinary situation. Now she was completely out of gas. She could lie down right there on the mudroom floor and take a snooze.

Instead, she went into the kitchen to brew fresh pots of coffee and hot chocolate.

Chapter Thirty-two

First, Maddox just lay there, catching his breath, allowing the warmth to sink into his body like melted butter on toast. (Cinnamon toast would be excellent right now.)

He'd never been so cold before, and the cold had made him frightened and confused. Standing on the street corner with the wind shoving him in the back like a giant saying *Go away, you're not wanted here,* he'd wished with all his heart to hear his father call him, to hear running footsteps, to be swept up into loving arms. He'd stood there, waiting, listening, hoping . . . and no one came.

His mother had warned him. 'Don't leave my side,'

she always said when they were in a store. 'Don't leave the yard on your own. It's easy to get lost.'

He had disobeyed her. His mommy often said, '*Now* look what happened!' when he'd done something wrong.

Now look what happened.

Out in the freezing dark, he'd been scared, shaking with cold and fright. Here, nestled in the sweet-smelling straw with Pooh's tiny body snuggled next to him, Maddox's spirits lifted. Even though there was no wall in front, it was still like being in a house. There was light from the spotlight. There were other people, too, kind of. Even if they were only statues, he felt less alone.

One problem: no food. Of course there wasn't any food, the statues of Mary, Joseph, and baby Jesus didn't require food.

He scrabbled in his pants pockets to see if he had any candy canes left, even a broken piece. But no. He'd eaten every bite. Hugging Pooh to him, he realized the dog was probably hungry, too. Pooh was so skinny. But what a good, loyal, friend! Maddox would *never* throw Pooh out into the cold night.

So he couldn't go home. Could he? If he went back, would they allow him to keep Pooh in the house just for a while?

If he tried, could he find his way back? He thought

so. Granddad's house was right up the street from the big brick Jared Coffin House, and that wasn't far away, was it?

Next to him, Pooh began to snore, a sweet rumbling sound that made Maddox grin. Relaxing into the straw, he realized he was awfully tired from all that running and carrying Pooh. Being warm made him drowsy.

A stick of straw poked his ear. He moved his head, trying to get comfortable, and sort of sat up, and sort of scanned the streets outside in case his daddy was out there looking for him.

The street was empty, except for the blowing snow.

His lower lip quivered. Tears filled his eyes. Sadness filled his heart. Snot filled his nose — unattractive, his mommy usually told him. He couldn't help it, though. He was scared.

Chapter Thirty-three

The baby slept, but Kennedy was a bubbling emotional geyser threatening to erupt momentarily.

She had a daughter. Joy!

Then terror blasted through her. *Maddox*. Her little boy.

Maddox had run away because she had been horrid to him. Shame, anguish, mommy guilt of the most torturous kind.

She'd given birth without James present. Heartbreak, disappointment, more guilt — couldn't she have waited?

Her mother had been present. Nicole had been helpful. Okay, more than helpful. Nicole had taken charge and conducted the entire chaotic mess with as much expertise as anyone could wish for. She had been an angel of

kindness. More guilt, because Kennedy had been such a beast to Nicole.

Her mother was on the floor again with more towels, soaking up the natural but still rather gruesome muck of childbirth. That in itself – her mother performing manual labor – filled Kennedy with incredulity. Katya did not enjoy housework. Never had. But Katya was humming a Christmas carol, and she looked exultant. Kennedy was confused.

Most of all, where was Maddox? Shouldn't her father and James have found her child and brought him back? She didn't want her son to believe that she'd blithely forgotten about him, or worse, tossed him away – 'You're a bad boy!' – then lay down and gotten herself another child. Her heart wrung with worry. She was glad to have a daughter, but so frightened for Maddox.

Was this family life at its most basic? A cauldron of constantly changing sensations? Kennedy was stunned to realize that she'd been in labor all day without realizing it because she'd been so overwhelmed with intense and often ungenerous emotions. How had her own mother maneuvered through family life so serenely, like a sailboat on a windless sea? How would Kennedy survive her own family life, especially if she was as self-centered and myopic as she'd been with little Maddox?

Her sweet little boy, her darling child, with his giggle, his innocence, his wide-eyed trust in his mommy. Her heart broke when she thought of the radiant confidence on his face when he watched her. She knew she'd been cranky with him lately, restless and uncomfortable in her own body. She'd tried to explain that to him, but how could a four-year-old possibly comprehend the discomfort of a pregnant woman? She'd been mad to think he could. She'd been awful to call him a bad boy. She'd been so out of her mind she hadn't even realized she was in labor.

Kennedy was mortified. Here she was, tucked up with her new baby in her arms, warm and well-cared-for, and her precious son was out there in the bitter stormy night. She should search for him. She struggled to sit up. Not a good idea.

'Mommy?' she quavered.

Katya responded instantly. 'Yes, sweetie?'

'Would you help James and Daddy search for Maddox? I'm so afraid. They should be back with him by now.'

Katya hesitated. 'Of course I'll go. But someone should stay with you. Would you rather Nicole searched and I stayed?'

Her mother's words appeared to be free of judgment.

'I suppose since Nicole's a nurse, and the baby is

so new, and I'm still a bit of a mess . . .' Kennedy let her voice trail off.

'You're right.' Katya rose to her feet. 'I'll put on my coat and help look for Maddox. Don't' worry, darling. We'll find him.'

'Thank you, Mommy.' Kennedy began to cry. What if they didn't find him? What if he was hiding in the dark garage of a summer family who had gone away? What if he developed pneumonia or hypothermia?

What if Maddox thought no one was looking for him? What if he thought that because she'd told him he was bad, she no longer loved him? She imagined her son cold, lost, and frightened, and sobs broke out, startling her newborn babe. But she couldn't stop crying.

Chapter Thirty-four

Nicole entered the living room to find Katya with her own arms full of stained cloths and towels.

'I got it as dry as I could.' Katya stared ruefully at the stained rug.

'It's fine,' Nicole told her. 'The heat of the fire will dry it, and we'll toss a throw rug over it. In fact, I know just the one. It's a Christmas rug my grandmother hooked for me, with snowmen and decorations on it.'

Katya, who had obviously recovered from her sentimental moment, looked horrified.

'Maddox will like it,' Nicole reminded her. 'He'll think it's a decoration and won't know what it's hiding.'

'Mommy's going to go look for Maddox,' Kennedy

said from the sofa. She was weeping steadily. 'They should be back by now.'

Nicole set the tray of warm drinks on the coffee table. Squeezing onto the sofa next to Kennedy, she lifted the young woman's arm and put her fingers on her wrist, taking her pulse.

'You're fine, Kennedy. I'm sure Maddox is fine, too. He can't have gone far. The three of us need to take a moment to settle down. We've all been part of a momentous occasion. Let's have some coffee – hot chocolate for you, Kennedy. If they're still not back by the time we've finished our drinks, Katya or I can go out and look, too.' She handed the drinks around.

Katya was content to let Nicole take charge. She sipped her coffee, so rich and fragrant, with the kick of Baileys in it. 'Alcohol?'

Nicole nodded. 'For medicinal purposes,' she said, not quite joking. She took a restoring sip of her own coffee.

Katya peered over at her granddaughter, tucked securely in Kennedy's arms. 'What is she doing?'

'She's sleeping,' Kennedy said. Glancing at Nicole, she asked, 'That's okay, right?'

'That's absolutely okay. She's probably tired, too. She's just been born. She's warm, she can smell her mommy, you're holding her next to your heart so she

can hear it beating, she's exactly where she should be.'

'If only Maddox were here,' Kennedy wept. 'Today's been such a *jumble*. I feel like I've done everything wrong. I can't even love this new baby as much as I should because I'm so frightened for Maddox.'

Katya chuckled. 'Mommy fear. It's the worst. I used to be terrified when you took gymnastics. I often had to leave the meet to throw up.'

'I never knew that,' Kennedy said.

Katya shrugged. 'I thought it would be unhealthy for you to be aware of my emotional turmoil.'

Kennedy gawped. 'You had emotional turmoil?'

Nicole hid her smile by drinking more coffee.

Katya rolled her eyes. Obviously the coffee had helped her regain her composure. 'Thank you for this most reviving drink, Nicole.' She emitted the most elegant, subtle of sighs. 'It will help. I promised Kennedy I'd help search for Maddox.'

'I'll go.' Nicole stood up. 'You should stay with your daughter.'

'But you're the nurse,' Katya reasoned. 'You should stay, in case something goes wrong.'

'Nothing will go wrong,' Nicole promised Katya. At the same time, a warmth flushed through her, not entirely caused by the Baileys and coffee. Katya trusted

her with her daughter and the new baby. Katya had stepped down from her pedestal. Perhaps they could never be friends, but possibly she and Kennedy's mother, Sebastian's former wife, could be allies.

Katya glanced toward the window, almost completely iced over by blowing snow. She shivered delicately. 'Perhaps I will stay here . . . with my daughter.'

Nicole didn't hesitate. 'Of course,' she agreed, heading to the hall and her coat.

Chapter Thirty-five

Snix snored so enormously he woke himself. It took him a moment to realize where he was – he'd slept in so many different places during his young life.

He was lying in straw inside a shed, warm as warm could be, cuddled next to his boy Maddox.

But Maddox was *crying*.

Snix sat up and licked Maddox's cheeks. The tears tasted salty and made Snix even hungrier.

'Oh, Pooh,' Maddox sniffled. 'I don't know what to do. I want my mommy and daddy. I want to go home.'

Snix sat up straight, attempting to look large and confident. For one thing, he knew he had to think of himself as *Pooh* if he wanted to stay with the boy,

and oh boy, did he want to stay with this boy. For another thing . . . well, what? What could he do?

He wagged his tail, hopefully. He gave a yip of encouragement. He tried to look bright-eyed.

His stomach growled.

Maddox's stomach growled.

Perhaps . . . Pooh chewed a stick of straw. Nope, didn't work. He spit it out.

Snow whirled into the shed, glittering in the glow from the spotlight.

'We've got to go back out there, Pooh.' Maddox stood up. 'We've got to go home.'

Pooh yapped once.

Maddox frowned. He thought out loud: 'I'm sure they'll take me back.' Looking down at Pooh, he clenched his fists. 'But I won't let them take you away from me, Pooh. I'll protect you. Even if we have to run away again.'

Pooh's heart sank. He wasn't sure he could survive much longer without food.

'MADDOX? MADDOX!'

Running footsteps came toward them. Snow exploded as four booted feet stomped through the drifts in front of the shed. Two huge figures fell on their knees.

'Maddox.' The boy's father reached out and clutched the boy to him. 'Maddox, hey guy, I'm so glad I

found you. What a smart kid you are to discover such a warm place to stay. Aren't you hungry? Don't you want to go home? Your mommy and grandmommy and Nicole are so worried about you. Granddad and I have been looking everywhere for you.'

Pooh watched as the boy's father ran his hands over the boy's head and body, as if checking to be certain he was still all there.

'I'm sorry, Daddy, don't be mad at me—'

'I'm not mad, Maddox. Granddad and I are so glad to find you—'

'Maddox, you need a hat. Take mine.' Granddad pulled his wool cap over the boy's head.

Pooh trembled as he heard the humans babble, everyone talking at once. The great big men had tears in their eyes. They hugged and touched Maddox as if he were the most precious thing in the world.

'Come on, Mad Man. We're going home. It's Christmas Eve.' The daddy lifted Maddox up in his arms and held him tight.

Pooh whimpered, just a tiny whimper that kind of slipped out . . .

'I want Pooh!' Maddox wriggled in his father's arms. 'I won't go without Pooh.'

Pooh shivered with hope and terror.

Two huge arms reached in and picked Pooh up.

'I've got Pooh,' the grandfather said. 'He's coming home with us, too.'

'*In the house*,' Maddox stipulated.

'Of course in the house,' said the daddy. 'We wouldn't leave a puppy out in the cold on a night like this.'

The granddaddy wrapped the outside of his coat around Pooh. 'We need to give this dog some food. I can feel his ribs.'

The men set off tramping through the falling snow. They passed Sweet Inspirations with its windows full of candy. They passed Zero Main with its bright Christmas wreath. They passed Petticoat Row Bakery with its windows full of gingersnaps and cookies shaped like stars. They zigzagged around the tall brick Jared Coffin House, which had been standing since 1845 and still stood undaunted in the ferocious blizzard.

Pooh could feel the granddaddy's heart beating. The man's arms were big and held him much more securely than Maddox's thin arms had done – not that Pooh was complaining about Maddox, who was his true champion and best friend.

They went up Centre Street, past the Congregational Church. They forked left onto Westchester. Most of the houses were dark and closed, but one house glowed with light.

'Back door,' the granddaddy yelled. 'We're covered

with snow. We can kick off our boots in the mudroom.'

Pooh sagged. His memories of the mudroom were not good ones. The woman who didn't like dogs, the yelling . . .

He had no choice. He could struggle out and run away, but where would he go? Surely this time they would allow him to stay.

Doors opened and closed. Pooh was set on the floor. Boots were kicked off, scattering snow onto the already wet throw rug.

Pooh saw a pair of men's feet in red socks leave the room. Then a man's feet in brown socks left.

'We found him!' the daddy yelled.

'Oh, thank heavens!' Voices poured from the front of the house.

'Good Lord!' one of the men cried.

Shouts of jubilation rose and what sounded like dozens of voices intertwined. A thin baby's wail sirened through the noise and the voices softened.

Pooh sat in the mudroom, dripping, probably smelling of wet dog hair, *alone*.

'This calls for champagne,' a man announced.

Footsteps grew closer to the kitchen. Pooh peered around the door. Only his nose and eyes . . .

'Hey, you.' The granddaddy saw Pooh looking.

Pooh flinched and went small.

The backyard was bordered by a fence and also by hedges with stubborn green-brown leaves hanging on to the brown twiggy branches. He could see where flowers had been in the summer, because the beds were edged with shells. A white birdbath stood at the other end of the yard. He ran through the brown grass to check – it had water in it, and a black feather. He picked out the feather and put it in his pocket. Returning to the flower beds bordering the lawn, he spent some time checking out the shells. Most were white, with pale purple streaks on the inside. Some had tips sharp enough to cut, others were rolled up like burritos. Here and there green or blue sea glass twinkled, edges smoothed to satin by the ocean waves.

A hawthorn tree grew at the end of the garden. It had a few red berries left. Nicole told him the birds liked the berries, so he liked the tree, even though its thorns made it impossible to climb.

It *was* cold out. He looked up and up, at the sky. It was white, heavy, and damp-looking, like a wet pillow. Maybe it would snow. He hoped so. His mommy said he'd seen snow before, but he couldn't remember. If it did snow, his fort would be a perfect place to keep warm, so he stomped over to the picnic table and benches.

It took him a few tries to wrestle the bench over so it was lying on its side, legs sticking out, the long

73

flat seat side acting like a wall. He stomped around to the other side and struggled to tip the other bench over. Finally he succeeded. He went to one end of the table and crawled under.

It wasn't much of a fort. The seats of the benches didn't come all the way up to the table top, so a long space was exposed on each side. The dry grass was crackly. He sat for a moment, considering what kind of fort it should be. Pirate? Spaceship? Indian?

A door opened. Nicole stepped out onto the porch, wearing a navy blue sweater with ice-skating penguins slipping and twirling all over it. The sweater made him laugh.

'Penguins don't ice-skate!' he called.

Nicole came down the steps. 'Oh, I wouldn't be so sure.' She headed toward the shed at the back of the garden and yanked the door open. 'Let's see what we've got for you.'

Maddox raced over to peer inside the dark enclosure. Reaching up, Nicole pulled a chain, and a light came on, a single bulb hanging from the ceiling. The building was wonderful, with a slate floor, high work benches along two walls, shelves along the third, and yard implements leaning on the fourth. He saw rakes, a lawn mower, shovels, saws. Coiled onto a special rack was a green garden hose. Pots, paint cans, and other containers sat on the shelves. Above them, outlined

'We didn't forget you.' The granddaddy lifted Pooh up, carried him a few feet, and set him down again. 'But we've got a new baby in the house, the prettiest little girl you've ever seen. My goodness, there is no end to the wonders that can happen. Leave the house for thirty minutes and come home to a granddaughter!' He poured milk into a bowl and set the bowl in the microwave. The man opened the freezer and scrabbled around, all the while singing 'Jingle Bells.'

Pooh reflected silently, but not unhappily, that human beings were odd.

'Here,' said the granddaddy. 'I warmed the milk in the microwave. Drink up while I thaw some meatloaf for you, little fellow. Don't tell Nicole. She won't miss it anyway, with all the food in the house. Now where's the champagne?'

Pooh lapped up the warm milk as fast as his pink tongue could go while the man gathered glasses and popped a cork and set them on a tray.

'Dinner is served, your majesty.' The man set a plate in front of Pooh. Suddenly, while Pooh watched, he pulled his sweater off over his head and piled it on the floor next to the vent. 'Here. When you're through eating, you can rest on this. I'm too damned hot with all this excitement.' He picked up the tray and started to leave the room. Stopping, he said to Pooh with a serious tone, 'No accidents now, okay?'

Pooh sat down, lifted his head into its most noble pose and remained still, doing the best he could to signal his comprehension and agreement.

The man chortled. 'You're a smart one, aren't you?' He hurried away.

Pooh dove into the plate of warm delicious meatloaf.

Chapter Thirty-six

The living room was crowded with people all talking at once. Nicole took off the coat she'd just put on and settled into a chair in the corner to watch the grand reunion. Kennedy handed the baby to Katya and opened her arms to Maddox who threw himself into her embrace. James stood swaying in front of the baby, looking so green Nicole thought he might vomit.

James fell on his knees in front of his wife and took her face in his hands.

'How did you do this?' he asked, his face shining with tears. 'We weren't gone more than half an hour, and you had the baby? Are you okay? Do you need to go to the hospital? It's a girl? How can it be a girl? Kennedy, I love you.'

Katya sank gracefully into another armchair, both arms supporting her tiny granddaughter. 'When I had Kennedy,' she mused aloud, 'I didn't *comprehend* her at first. I was sort of dozy on painkillers of some sort. Look at this splendid infant. She seems so peaceful.'

Maddox squirmed away from his mother and ran to Katya. 'Let me see her, Grandmama.'

Katya held the bundle out for Maddox to see. 'Careful,' she warned. 'The baby is brand-new and fragile.'

As she viewed the lucky family – James with Kennedy, Katya with Maddox and the baby, Nicole allowed herself a moment of self-indulgence. She was spent. The adrenaline and calm ecstasy of practiced, knowledgeable, focused skill that had flooded her when Kennedy began to give birth drained away now, leaving her limp. She was not as young as she used to be. She'd done all the kneeling and bracing and assisting and cleaning with the swift ease of a ballerina, but right now her joints and muscles informed her they needed a nice hot bath with Epsom salts.

Her emotions were in upheaval, too. The birth of a baby was always – to use a terribly overused word – an *awesome* event. She hadn't recovered yet from the anxiety, like background music in her mind, that something was wrong with Kennedy or the baby, or could go wrong during the delivery, or, she hardly

dared think it, that *she* could have done something wrong. If she hadn't been a trained nurse and a mature adult, she would have shrieked and screamed right along with Kennedy all through the delivery. The effort of pretending to be calm had taken its toll on her strength.

She could scarcely summon up the energy to keep the proper expression on her face, a smile that asserted 'I'm so happy for you all,' instead of a childish pout declaring 'Doesn't anyone care about *me*?' and she felt wearily guilty about that.

Sebastian entered the living room with a tray of flutes and an opened bottle of champagne. He set it on the side table by the window. 'Champagne for everyone.'

'Even me?' Maddox asked.

Sebastian and the other adults laughed indulgently.

'It's a special day, so you may have a sip of mine,' James told his son.

Sebastian couldn't stop smiling. He stepped away from the table for a moment, drawn inexorably to the sight of his granddaughter. He leaned over the back of the chair where Katya sat holding the baby while Maddox raised himself up on tiptoes to peek at the blanketed bundle.

There they were, Nicole thought. Everyone together who belongs together. By the window, the tall Christmas

tree she'd decorated twinkled like love made visible. In the fireplace the logs burned low, crackling with sparks as the bark snapped. Stockings hung from the mantel. The crèche sat in perfection on the table. Nicole didn't belong in this intimate, elementary family group. She had learned in harder times how to steel her heart, and now she did her best to remember. She took deep breaths. She tried to count her blessings.

The phone rang.

'The phones are working again,' Nicole noted to no one in particular.

Sebastian answered. His tense shoulders softened. 'Katya? It's for you.'

Katya hesitated, briefly, before laying the baby in James's arms. She reached for the phone.

'Hello?' Katya's voice was wary.

While the others watched, Katya's face began to glow. 'Yes, I miss you, too. Wait a moment.' Putting her hand over the receiver, she said, 'It's Alonzo. I'll take this into the other room.' She left, head high, triumphant.

Father Christmas, I owe you one, Nicole thought. Exchanging glances with Sebastian, she could see he was thinking the same thing.

Suddenly, Maddox flew across the room and pitched himself at Nicole. Hauling himself up onto her lap, the little boy leaned against her. 'Nicole, Pooh is in the kitchen,' he whispered.

Maddox's sweet breath in her ear, his easy confidence in her being his friend, expanded Nicole's heart into confetti and fireworks. For a moment, she couldn't speak.

She cleared her throat. 'That's wonderful, Maddox. Is he okay?'

'Yes. I kept him warm all through the storm.'

'Maybe he needs something to eat,' Nicole suggested.

'Oh, yes!'

Sebastian was pouring the champagne and handing it around.

'I'll be right back for mine,' Nicole told him.

Maddox took her hand and pulled her from the room, down the hall to the kitchen, where Pooh lay curled up on Sebastian's sweater, snoring, deeply asleep. An empty bowl and plate were on the floor.

'It looks like Granddad has already fed Pooh,' Nicole said. Dropping down to Maddox's level, she put her hands on his shoulders. 'You must be hungry, too, after your adventures. Can I fix you something?'

Maddox's eyes sparkled. 'You make the best grilled cheeses, Nicole.'

'Then I'll make you one right now,' she said, and set to work, while Maddox sat next to Pooh, scratching him softly just behind the ears.

Chapter Thirty-seven

Christmas Eve passed in a blur for Kennedy.
While her father drove off in the blizzard to fetch a friend of his who was a physician, James helped her into their bedroom so she could shower and slip on her maternity nightgown. Dr Morris turned out to be an older woman, even calmer than Nicole, with gentle hands and a way of humming when she examined Kennedy. Not only did she pronounce Kennedy in A-plus condition, she presented her with a box of pads she'd brought from the hospital, a great relief for Kennedy on this night when every drugstore in town was shut tight. Overloaded with emotion and the drama of the evening, Kennedy thought that this humble, ordinary gift meant more than silver and gold.

Dr Morris checked the baby, proclaiming her perfectly healthy. She put the necessary antibiotic ointment on her eyes, before, obviously pleased to be so useful, presenting Kennedy with a bag she'd prepared at the hospital. It held disposable diapers, tiny cotton shirts and several sleep rompers with infinitely small cotton cuffs that folded over the baby's hands to prevent her from scratching her face.

After Sebastian drove Dr Morris home, Nicole set out a buffet on the dining room table: the beef Wellington sliced into pieces, vegetables, warm bread. No one sat at the table, but wandered here and there with a plate and a glass, perching on the edge of a chair, saying over and over again, 'Isn't it amazing? Can you believe she's here? And on Christmas Eve!' Everyone was still animated and vaguely flustered, constantly peeking at the baby as if to be certain she really existed.

After some discussion, James helped Maddox rouse the sleepy little dog and take him out into the backyard where the animal performed his physical duties with alacrity, then raced back into the house. Tonight, James and Kennedy agreed, during a private conference, Pooh could sleep on the floor in Maddox's bedroom. After all, Kennedy thought with a private, slightly guilty smugness, if the dog did something on the rug, it wouldn't be her job to deal with it.

Because Pooh was allowed to sleep in his room, Maddox went to bed easily, and after his adventurous evening, he fell asleep at once. The dog, James told Kennedy, curled up on the rug next to the bed as if he considered himself Maddox's protector.

Kennedy was thankful that Maddox had the animal at least for a few nights. It would keep him from feeling excluded in the commotion over the new baby. Perhaps she'd even let him keep the dog.

Kennedy was utterly drained. Her head swam with the buzz of her family's conversation. People loomed up at her like boats through the fog.

'How is she?' Sebastian asked, or James, or Katya.

'Is she still sleeping?' Katya inquired, or Sebastian, or James.

'Would you like me to hold her while you eat?' offered James, or Katya, or Sebastian.

Nicole came to her rescue. 'Kennedy, you shouldn't overexert yourself. It's time for you to get in bed and go to sleep.'

'But the baby, where will she sleep?' Kennedy worried.

'In a dresser drawer, just as infants have throughout the centuries.'

Kennedy recoiled with dismay. 'The wood will be so hard.'

Nicole shook her head. 'I've lined it with quilts.

in white chalk, were the tools: hammers, pliers, wrenches, screwdrivers. He wanted to get them down and *do* something.

Nicole said, 'Look, here: the folding lawn chairs I told you about. See?' Picking up an aluminum chair with webbed seat and back, she opened it, and turned it sideways, to display how it could be used as a wall.

Maddox nodded. 'Cool.'

'Shall we take them out?'

Maddox nodded again.

Nicole hoisted two chairs, one under each arm. Maddox took a third chair, which was surprisingly lightweight, holding it as well as he could in front of him, following Nicole back to the picnic table. Returning to the shed, Nicole reached up to lift a couple of fat vinyl cushions from a shelf.

'These might be good as seats in your fort,' she told him.

Maddox grinned. 'Oh, yeah.'

She tossed him one and carried two out herself. She dropped them outside the fort, seeming to understand how private the enterprise was to him. He wanted to arrange things himself, even if it took him time and struggle.

Back in the shed, Nicole stood with her hands on her hips and scanned the walls. 'Let's see. What else?' Cocking her head, she suggested, 'What about these?'

Besides, she'll probably end up in bed with you and
James.'

Nicole showed Kennedy how to wrap the baby
'like a burrito' – so snugly the baby felt as contently
secure as she had been in Kennedy's belly.

'Now go to bed and get some sleep. We're not as
wiped out as you are. In fact, we're all rather overexcited. So until we all go to bed,' Nicole told
Kennedy, 'someone out here in the living room will
hold your baby.'

'I want to hold her,' Kennedy confessed. 'I don't
want to let her go.'

'The best thing you can do for her now,' Nicole
assured her, 'is sleep.'

'I'll see you in the morning, darling.' Katya kissed
Kennedy's forehead. 'Before I leave for Boston.'

Nothing had ever felt as soft as the plump mattress
Kennedy lay on. Clouds, or perhaps it was a down
comforter, warmed her weary body. Sleep came at
once.

And a good thing, for when the baby's thin cry
from the drawer woke her at four in the morning,
everyone else was asleep. Next to her on the bed, James
snored loudly, a chainsaw noise that drowned out his
daughter's cries.

Kennedy lifted her daughter from the dresser drawer
and carried her into the living room. She changed her

diaper and wrapped her snugly again. She decided to rest on the sofa, holding the infant in her arms.

The windows were black with deep night. The blizzard had passed. The wind was gone. It was silent throughout the house and over the island. The fire had burned out in the fireplace, but the room was still warm. Kennedy turned on the lights of the Christmas tree to keep her company as she rested with her babe in her arms.

She couldn't believe her good fortune. Now she had a son and a daughter, and a husband who loved them. Her mother was leaving in the morning to meet Alonzo in Boston. And now she could finally admit it: Kennedy had never seen her father look so happy as when he was with Nicole.

As for Nicole – all Kennedy's animosity had vanished, replaced by the cheering assurance that she would have her father's new, steady-handed and knowledgeable wife in her life as she went forward as a mother. She wished she had some way to thank Nicole, to express her inexpressible appreciation for all she'd done. What could she possibly do to articulate her gratitude?

In the morning, Kennedy decided sleepily, she'd tell James what she'd like to name their new daughter.

Nicole Katya Noel.